COLLINS GUIDE
TO THE SEA FISHES

of
Britain and North-Western Europe

Bent J. Muus

Illustrated by
Preben Dahlstrom

Translated by
Gwynne Vevers

Collins
St James's Place, London

ISBN 0 00 219258 6

HAVFISK OG FISKERI was
first published in Denmark
by G.E.C. Gads Forlag in 1964

© G.E.C. Gads Forlag 1964

© In the English translation
Wm. Collins Sons and Co. Ltd. 1974

First published in Great Britain 1974
Reprinted 1977

Colour plates printed in Denmark by
F.E. Bording

Text printed in Great Britain by
Collins Clear-Type Press,
London and Glasgow

Foreword

This richly illustrated handbook provides a brief and understandable introduction to the structure, habits, distribution and economic importance of the fishes of the North-east Atlantic Ocean. The text has been written by Bent J. Muus of the Danish Institute of Fisheries and Marine Research and the illustrations have been prepared by Preben Dahlstrom. From the start it was not intended that the fishes should be shown in their natural colours but rather as they are seen in practice, that is when freshly caught and with slightly faded colours. The numerous pictures at the head of each section and the text illustrations are either original drawings or they have been adapted from material in the literature.

Originally all the colour plates in this book were to be prepared only from freshly caught specimens, but it turned out that even a period of 2½ years was too short for all the necessary material to be collected. Nevertheless, 142 species out of a total of 173 were drawn from fresh specimens and for this the authors are primarily grateful for the great assistance they have received from many marine biological institutes and fishing ports in Norway, Denmark and France.

Contents

Portrait of a fish | 5
Biology of fishes | 11
Identification keys | 20
Illustrated descriptions | 29
History of marine fisheries | 208
Capture techniques | 215
Fishing industry | 229
Fisheries biology | 234
Index | 241

This book is intended for all those
interested in the beauty and wonder of the
world of fishes. The simple identification
keys, with over 150 sketches, will enable
the reader rapidly to identify the
individual species and then to turn to the
relevant descriptions for greater detail on
habits, occurrences, method of capture
and economic value.

Bent Muus
Preben Dahlstrom

PORTRAIT OF A FISH

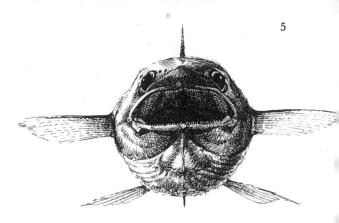

In the course of time the word 'fish' has acquired a much more exact meaning than it had in former times. It was once possible to apply the term fish to all kinds of marine animal, whether worm, sea-star, seal or whale. Nowadays, we can restrict the term to gill-breathing vertebrate animals with fins, which are tied to an aquatic life. In other words, the fishes are related to the amphibians, reptiles, birds and mammals. They are, therefore, more familiar to us than the other, often specialised forms of marine life.

There are about 20,000 different living species of fish in the world, and new species are being discovered every year. Although·the external appearance of the different species is extremely variable— and indeed many look very peculiar—it is soon apparent that they are all merely variations on a fairly simple basic plan. This will be understandable if we look at a typical bony fish.

As already mentioned, one of the characteristic features of a fish is the possession of fins, which are folds of skin stretched like sails over a skeleton of fin rays. These rays may be either stiff like spines (spiny or hard rays) or soft and jointed, simple or branched (articulated rays). As a rule there is a joint at the base of each ray, so that with the help of small muscles the fin can at will be folded or unfolded.

The sketch below shows that the dorsal, caudal and anal fins are unpaired, whereas the pectoral and ventral fins are paired

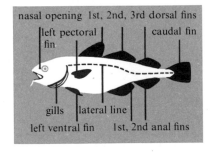

structures. The paired fins correspond to the fore-limbs and hind-limbs of the higher vertebrates.

In many but not all fishes there is a distinct line, known as the lateral line, extending from the head to the tail; this contains a series of small sense organs. The actual course of the lateral line plays an important part in the identification of fish species.

In the cyclostomes (lampreys and hagfishes) and selachians (sharks and rays)

spiny rays   articulated rays

each gill opens separately to the outside world, but in the bony fishes the gills and gill slits are protected by gill covers. Each gill cover or operculum consists of thin bony plates which are often armed with spines and thorns. The lower and rear edges of the gill cover are free, so that the water sucked into the mouth can be forced out backwards after it has passed over the gills where it is used in respiration.

Skin and scales

The outer skin or epidermis of a fish secretes a large amount of mucus which serves partly to reduce the frictional resistance of the water and partly as a barrier to parasites, making it difficult for these organisms to settle on the skin. The mucus also provides good protection against various kinds of toxic substances. The thin and transparent epidermis covers the scales which are ossifications of the underlying layer, the corium. Only a few fishes, e.g. the conger eel, lack scales. In other species, scales may be absent from certain parts of the body. The scales grow with the fish and, like a tree trunk, they form growth rings which can be used for age determination. Sharks and rays do not have scales of this type, but are covered with numerous, usually sharp denticles, which account for the fact

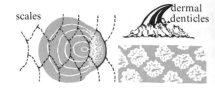

scales · dermal denticles

that a shark's skin feels like coarse sandpaper.

Scales are also lacking from very young fish, and are only developed when the fish has reached a certain length.

General anatomy

The skeleton of a fish consists of a cranium, a backbone or vertebral column and a large number of bones supporting the body and fins.

The cranium or skull is composed of the brain case and the mouth-gill apparatus, the latter consisting of supporting bony arches which are movably hinged at the underside of the brain case. The vertebral column supports the skeleton of the unpaired fins and the ribs, while the paired fins have their own supporting skeleton which is only loosely connected with the main skeleton.

The majority of fishes have bones in the mouth cavity which are provided with

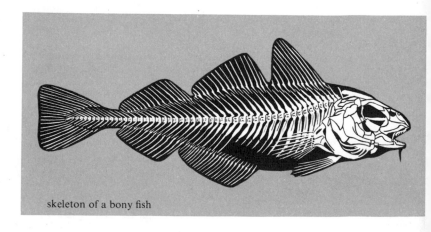

skeleton of a bony fish

numerous teeth, and these are sometimes so densely arranged as to form a covering to the bones concerned. The teeth may be pointed like an awl, broad like a chisel or quite flat and adapted for crushing.

The oesophagus connects the mouth to the stomach. In fish groups in which the stomach is lacking (e.g. members of the carp family) the oesophagus leads direct to the intestine. Close to the stomach there is, in bony fishes, a bundle of short blind sacs or coeca. The liver is usually very large and it contains a reserve store of fat with a high concentration of vitamins A and D.

The gills consist of thin-walled folds of

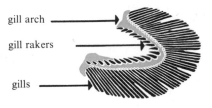

gill arch

gill rakers

gills

skin (lamellae), with a rich blood supply, and they are supported by cartilaginous gill arches. Water for respiration is taken in at the mouth and passed over the gill lamellae where the blood takes up oxygen from the water and releases carbon dioxide

into it. Fast-moving fishes, such as mackerel, swim with the mouth half open, and thus have a constant stream of water passing over their gills.

Many fishes possess a gas-filled swimbladder which serves as a buoyancy organ. In some groups there is a connection between the fore-gut and the swimbladder, and this enables the fish rapidly to release excess gas or to take into the bladder air swallowed at the water surface. In fishes without such an air duct the pressure in the swimbladder is adjusted by special areas on its walls in which the blood absorbs or secretes gases.

When a fish moves down into greater depths it quickly becomes subject to a greater pressure on its body, and the gas in the swimbladder is compressed.

It must, therefore, release more gas into the swimbladder in order to remain buoyant. The reverse takes place when a fish caught at a great depth is rapidly hauled to the surface: the water pressure is quickly reduced, the gas in the swimbladder expands, so that the fish has no time to absorb the excess gas into its blood, and the expanding swimbladder will then press the fore-gut out of the mouth. Cyclostomes, sharks, rays, mackerel, flatfishes and many deep-sea fishes have no swimbladder.

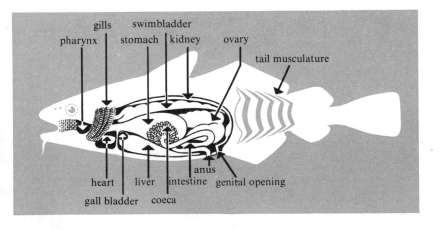

The body musculature is arranged symmetrically to the right and left of the vertebral column, and is divided into plate-like sections by thin transverse septa. This is why the muscle sections (or myotomes) of a cooked fish fall apart so readily.

Fish flesh has a relatively poor supply of blood and is usually white. However, fast-swimming fishes have a more rapid metabolism and a better blood supply for their muscles. Their flesh therefore has dark areas or is reddish (e.g. in the tunny).

Sense organs

Most fishes are rather short-sighted, even when their eyes are positioned for distant vision. On the basis of their structure the eyes of fishes are well adapted to perceive movements, but they are not so good at perceiving the shape of objects. Fishes

Mammalian eye, in which lens shape is changed

Fish eye, in which lens position is changed

living close to the water surface often have the best visual acuity. Selachians can only perceive differences in light intensity. Bony fishes, however, have well-developed colour vision. No fish species, however, can perceive colour and form well enough

to distinguish an angler's artificial fly from a real fly.

In addition, many fishes possess a characteristic apparatus, the lateral line, which consists of a row of small sense organs and is visible externally as a conspicuous stripe along each side of the body; it divides into numerous branches on the head. Experiments have shown that the lateral line enables the fish to perceive and identify the direction of pressure waves produced by movements in the water (other fish, enemies). As the lateral line also picks up an echo of its own movements it helps the fish to fix the position of stationary objects; it therefore reinforces the fish's vision.

Fishes can also hear, but the extent to which they can do so varies considerably according to the family to which they belong. The carp-like fishes have the best sense of hearing, for their inner ear is connected mechanically to the swimbladder by certain small bones. The gas-filled swimbladder is made to vibrate by sound waves and these fluctuations are transmitted to the ear by the small bones. The herring has a similarly functioning, although structurally different mechanism for the better reception of sound.

As in the other vertebrates the characteristically constructed auditory organ is the receiving apparatus for sound waves (see p. 61), and it also functions as an organ of balance.

Knowing that fishes can hear, it is only natural to ask whether they can also produce sounds. Some fish groups (horse mackerel, porcupine fish) do this, producing 'tooth-grinding' noises which are amplified by the resonance of the swimbladder. Other fish sounds are produced by the expulsion of air bubbles from the mouth (eels, minnows). In some catfishes, drums and gurnards sounds are produced by a special mechanism which vibrates the walls of the swimbladder.

We still do not know how many fish species are able to produce sounds, and only a few cases have been fully investigated. The 'language' of fishes presumably serves as a means of communication, particularly during the breeding season. In addition, it is probably used in driving off enemies or in keeping the shoal together.

Fishes have a good sense of smell. On each side in front of the eyes there are nasal openings each leading into an olfactory pit. A septum divides each nasal opening into two sections: during swimming, or by active pumping, water enters the olfactory pit through the front opening and leaves by the rear opening. In carti-

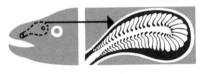

laginous fishes (selachians) the olfactory organs lie beneath the snout, near the mouth.

Its sense of smell enables a fish to differentiate between friend and foe and helps it to find its food. This is also reinforced by the sense of taste, which is localised, not only in the mouth, but also on the barbels, on the head and on a considerable part of the body surface.

Coloration

If one examines one of the colour plates in this book through a lens it will be found that, for example, the green colours are made up of tiny blue and yellow dots. In the same way the blackish-brown, yellow

Chromatophores and colour change

and red pigmentary colours of fishes are distributed among thousands of colour cells or chromatophores. When, for instance, the black pigment granules in a chromatophore are dispersed the cell will be black, but when these granules are gathered together into a tiny point the cell will not appear black. By this kind of mechanism the different colours can be made to appear and disappear.

Many bottom-living fishes, such as flatfishes, camouflage themselves by taking on the colour and pattern of the substrate. This colour change is under the control of the hormones and the nervous system. Experiments with blinded fish have shown that colour change is indirectly controlled through the eyes.

Almost all fishes that live in the upper water layers have pale, silvery sides to the body. This coloration depends upon the reflection of light from colourless, microscopic crystals which are deposited in the chromatophores of the dermis. These crystals consist of guanin, a by-product of metabolism. Deep-sea fishes are often dark, whereas those living among seaweeds have green or brown protective coloration. Finally, many fishes assume a nuptial coloration during the breeding period, and this may serve to attract a partner or to drive away rivals (sticklebacks, salmon).

body form. They have evolved, usually at the cost of their swimming efficiency, other features that are advantageous to them. High-backed fishes are certainly easy to see from the side, but difficult to recognise from other angles. Bottom-living fishes, such as rays and flatfishes, which lie partially buried themselves in the sand, often have a completely compressed body. On the other hand, predatory fishes, such as the angler and the cottids, which lie in wait for their prey, have a short, club-

Body form and swimming

During the course of evolution, high speed with a minimum expenditure of energy has been developed by mackerel, by penguins and dolphins and even by submarines, and this is reflected in many ways in their external form.

Many fishes, however are not torpedo-shaped, but have a completely different

shaped body with a very large head and mouth. Other fishes that mainly swim just above the bottom have long, snake-like bodies with very elongated dorsal and anal fins (eels, eelpouts and butterfish). Some

species have an armour of bony plates and spines and are so stoutly built that they would be difficult for a predatory fish to swallow (e.g. the lumpsucker).

The majority of fishes swim by lateral undulations of the body. Exceptions to

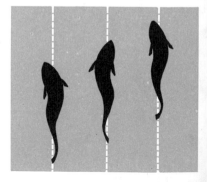

this are, for example, the pipefishes and sea-horses which swim by the undulations of the dorsal fin. In fish species with long dorsal and anal fins these may produce undulatory movements which drive the fish forwards or backwards. In slow swimming the pectoral fins help in steering, but they may also be used as paddles or for braking. The ventral fins are primarily passive stabilising organs, but in certain species they have become modified for a particular purpose, for example as a suction organ in gobies and the lumpsucker. For a short rapid forward movement a fish can expel water through the gill covers, thus producing a backward jet to give forward propulsion.

Fishes normally swim with the dorsal side upwards. Adult flatfishes, however, swim on one side, and some fishes such as the sea-horses swim in an upright position. There is also an African freshwater catfish that swims belly upwards. Many fishes can leap out of the water, e.g. salmon and flyingfishes. The tropical mudskippers leap about actively on land and even climb on to trees and bushes near the water.

Swordfishes and the larger members of the mackerel family are among the fastest swimming fishes. Bonitos can keep pace for hours with a ship travelling at 20 knots (c. 37 km per hour), and tunny are even faster.

Mackerel probably keep swimming throughout their life, but most fishes alternate, during a 24-hour period, between active swimming and periods of rest, during which they scarcely move. Indeed, there are even fishes, such as some of the wrasses, which lie on one side when resting.

BIOLOGY OF FISHES

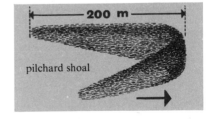

pilchard shoal

Shoaling

Many fishes, like some birds and mammals, congregate in large groups, usually known as shoals or schools. There are many different kinds of shoal, among the best known being those of the herring and mackerel, to which a fish will belong for the whole of its life. Other fishes, such as the two-spot goby, only come together when frightened and then only for a few seconds. The fishes in a shoal are usually of the same size (and the same age). Most fish shoals consist of only a single species, but in some cases they may also contain a small number of other social fishes. For instance, a shoal of sprats will often include a number of young herring.

The young fish of many species congregate in shoals; as they grow they tend to become more solitary and the shoal gradually breaks up. The three-spined stickleback forms shoals which break up for feeding and mating.

Vision is of great importance in the maintenance of a shoal; during the night shoals will break up and blinded fish are no longer capable of forming a shoal.

Shoal formation in fishes is based on several different instincts. Shoaling provides a certain amount of protection against enemies, for several pairs of eyes will see more than one pair and a large number of individuals appears to confuse an attacking predator. The importance of shoal formation during the breeding period is obvious.

Stationary and migratory fishes

Cottids, gobies, eelpouts and many other bottom-living fishes do not move far from the area in which they have grown up. At the most they may move into deeper water during the cold part of the year. This applies also to many flatfishes and to the local populations of coastal herring and cod which live in certain bays and fjords. These stationary fishes tend to evolve local races to a greater extent than the migratory species; such races can be distinguished on the basis of external and internal characters, such as the number of vertebrae and fin rays. These characters can usually only be used when subjected to statistical analysis; thousands of fish have to be examined in order to establish a reliable basis for race recognition.

A great number of the most important economic fishes are migratory, undertaking seasonal migrations, often for thousands of kilometres within their distribution range. In this context one thinks of the migrations of pilchard, herring, mackerel, tunny and cod.

Migration serves two main purposes: the search for food and breeding. After spawn-

ing in the Mediterranean the tunny are emaciated and hungry. They then move north during the summer months, where they enter waters that are rich in fish. By July they have reached the coasts of Norway, and as soon as the weather becomes cooler they turn round and move south again. In the next spring they move to their spawning grounds in the Mediterranean Sea. They, therefore, migrate more or less in a circle, and this is characteristic of many fish migrations: a constant, seasonally influenced movement between

spawning and feeding grounds with an overwintering place somewhere in between.

Among fishes it is quite common and indeed characteristic for spawning to take place in one area and for the young to grow up in another. The plaice spawns in the North Sea in depths of 25–75 m. The eggs drift passively in the sea for almost three weeks, but the newly hatched fry can swim and, with the help of sea currents, they move into shallow water. This is why young plaice spend their first months in shallow water off the beaches of the North Sea and western Baltic Sea. As they grow they move into deeper water and eventually distribute themselves in depths of 5–15 m.

Sprat fry move from the spawning grounds in the Skagerrak along the south-western coast of Norway, while young cod move from the Lofotens to the coasts of Finnmark. The migration routes of fishes are primarily determined by hydrographic factors (water temperature, currents, depths and bottom conditions; see p. 18).

The reproductive organs or gonads of bony fishes are in the form of hollow sacs which produce the eggs or sperm on their internal walls. In immature fishes these organs are still very small, but as they become mature the gonads become swollen with the sexual products. At spawning time these products are expelled through a short duct directly behind the anus.

As the gonads become mature the fish move to suitable spawning grounds. This book cites many examples of the particular requirements of different fish species.

Some species, for example, are dependent upon a very restricted temperature range, spawning only within a range of a few degrees. Cod spawn at 4–6°C, mackerel at about 12°C.

As a rule the eggs and sperm are released into the open water, while the parent fish swim alongside each other, sometimes belly to belly (as for example in cod and dragonet). In some fish, however, there are copulatory organs; the eggs are then fertilised within the body of the female (father lasher, redfish, sharks, rays).

The eggs are transparent and greenish or reddish. Many fish eggs are somewhat lighter than water and float slowly to the water surface (sprat, cod and flatfishes), others sink to the bottom (herring eggs) or adhere by means of tiny sticky filaments to seaweed (garfish). A great number of the free-floating (pelagic) eggs perish in bad weather or are eaten. Many newly hatched fish larvae die of starvation if there is insufficient food in the water, and so the number of such eggs produced must be very large. As far as is known the record is held by the sunfish with 300 million eggs. According to its size a plaice lays 50,000 to 500,000 eggs.

A number of fishes that spawn near the coast practise brood protection. The lumpsucker guards its egg clump against enemies, the gobies hide their eggs on the underside of bivalve mollusc shells, while sticklebacks build nests. In this way the eggs are protected from enemies, and the number of eggs may then be only a few hundred. Sharks give birth to 4–20 largish young.

Most fishes spawn each year, some dying after spawning. In every case the breeding period entails a very great expenditure of energy, so that after spawning the fish are thin, exhausted and hungry. Many fishes eat little or nothing during the spawning period.

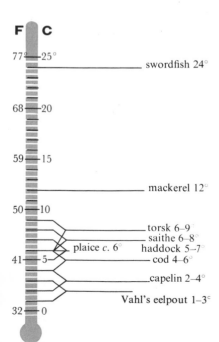

F   C

77° — 25°

————————————— swordfish 24°

68 — 20

59 — 15

————————————— mackerel 12°

50 — 10

————————— torsk 6–9°
————————— saithe 6–8°
plaice c. 6°   haddock 5–7°
41 — 5 ——————— cod 4–6°

——————— capelin 2–4°

Vahl's eelpout 1–3°

32 — 0

14

Early development

After fertilisation the egg develops into an embryo which grows at the expense of its yolk sac, which it gradually encircles and absorbs into its stomach. Development depends on the temperature and lasts from a few days up to several months, according to the species.

The newly hatched young fish is often very unlike the adult, and it is known as a larva. Before it becomes similar in appearance to the adults it has to undergo metamorphosis. The identification and development of fish larvae is an interesting but difficult subject. Among the more peculiar larval forms are those of the sunfish and of the angler (p. 195). Com-

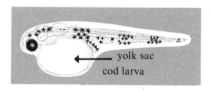
yolk sac
cod larva

plete developmental series are shown under the eel (p. 83), herring (p. 65), cod (p. 99) and plaice (p. 187).

Many fishes pay no attention at all to their offspring, which have to survive as best they can.

Fish larvae are usually pelagic and spend their time in the upper water layers. For the first few days after hatching they feed on the remains of the yolk and subsequently on tiny planktonic organisms. Their swimming abilities are still very poorly developed, so the larvae drift with the currents.

After some weeks of larval life, the larvae of bottom-living fishes move to the sea floor, often in quite shallow water. The young of flatfishes pass through their strange metamorphosis to the adult stage, as described for the plaice (p. 184). The young of pelagic species form shoals near the coast (e.g. herring) or move into deeper

water (e.g. sunfish, swordfish). By this stage the young will have metamorphosed and look like miniature editions of the adults.

Growth and longevity

Growth is, naturally, dependent primarily upon the availability of food and on the temperature, but it varies considerably from species to species; at an age of three years a mackerel has reached a length of 30 cm, whereas a close relative, the tunny, would then measure 100 cm. The weights of many fishes are given in this book. Fishes grow throughout life, but fastest when they are young. It is, therefore, difficult to state how large any given species can grow and the figures given here for maximum length and weight only mean that fish with measurements of that order or even larger are very rare.

Growth is slow in winter, and faster in summer. A fish also grows more slowly just before the spawning period when a large proportion of its food will be used for the build-up of the sexual products. There are only slight differences in growth rate between males and females. In eels and flatfishes the females are usually somewhat larger than the males.

The relation between the length and weight of a fish may be expressed according to the following formula: weight = a $\times L^n$, where a is a constant, L the length and n is usually 3, since growth is three-

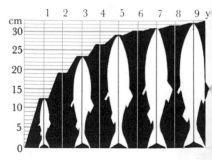

dimensional, whereas the length is a measure of one dimension only.

A number of gobies and pipefishes only live for one year, but many fishes have a life span of over 20 years, as for example, the Greenland shark, eel, cod, redfish, halibut and plaice. The sturgeon is said to reach an age of over 100 years. The determination of age and growth rate is of great importance in fisheries investigations and will be discussed in greater detail on p. 235.

Nutrition

Almost all marine fishes feed on animal food; vegetarians are found mainly in fresh waters. Among the typical predators that feed on other fishes are the tunny and many of the sharks. Other fishes only become predatory with age; many cod and redfish, for example, feed mainly on herring and capelin when they are old.

Predatory fishes feed mainly on small species that occur in large numbers: pilchards, herring, sprats, capelin, sand-eels, dragonets and gobies. The tunny evidently has a preference for other predatory fishes, such as mackerel, saury and garfish.

The majority of fishes feed chiefly on invertebrates, and particularly on members of three main animal groups. These are the *crustaceans* which play a comparable role in the sea to the insects on land, the *polychaete worms* which are eaten by practically all bottom-living fishes, and the *molluscs* (snails and bivalves) with thin shells which are easy to crush. The wolf-fish, however, has such powerful teeth (see fig. 117b, p. 153) that it can even deal with thick-shelled molluscs.

Other bottom-living animals that are important as fish food are the echinoderms, a group that includes the sea-stars, brittle-stars, sea-urchins and sea-cucumbers. The echinoderms are, however, poor in nutritional value and so they are only eaten in areas where there is a shortage of

crustaceans, worms and molluscs. Fishes living at or near the surface find their food visually, but many bottom-living species depend on the sense organs on their

crustaceans (18,000 marine species)

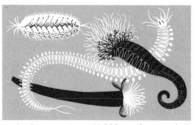

polychaete worms (4,000 marine species)

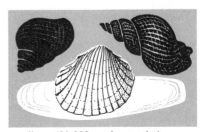

molluscs (91,000 marine species)

barbels (e.g. in the cod family). Flatfishes have special sensory cells on the underside of the head.

echinoderms (6,000 species, all marine)

Plankton and food chains

The term plankton is used for those plant and animal organisms, mostly very tiny, that drift more or less passively with the sea currents.

Plant plankton (phytoplankton) is found at or near the surface since, like most other plants, it is dependent upon energy from the sun. It uses the nutrient salts and carbon dioxide to synthesise organic matter. It consists mainly of microscopically small, one-celled algae, most of which measure only 1/10 to 1/1000 mm. The most important components of the phytoplankton are the diatoms, the dinoflagellates and the coccolithophores. Because of their immense numbers and their rapid multiplication, and in spite of their small size, these organisms form the basis for the nutrition of all marine animals.

Plant plankton is eaten by animal plankton (zooplankton) such as the pelagic crustaceans, pteropods and medusae or jellyfishes. The zooplankton also includes numerous pelagic worms and also the eggs and larvae of fishes and of bottom-living invertebrates.

The principal direct consumers of the phytoplankton are crustaceans such as the copepods (1–4 mm long) and the euphausians (7–40 mm long). These crustaceans and their larvae are in turn eaten by other planktonic animals, including pelagic fish larvae.

Many adult fishes feed mainly on planktonic organisms. This applies, for example, to herring, capelin, mackerel and also to many large fishes such as basking shark and sunfish. In addition, of course, the enormous whalebone whales feed on plankton.

Animals living on the sea floor also feed, directly or indirectly, on the plankton. A continuous rain of food remains, faeces and dead organisms, known collectively as detritus, falls to the bottom of the sea from the productive plankton layer. On the bottom this detritus is decomposed by bacteria and much is used as food by various bivalve molluscs, worms and crustaceans.

Within the fish's body the food is converted partly into energy and partly into growth. By comparing the amount of food consumed with the increase in weight of a fish one can obtain an idea of the efficiency of metabolism. If, for example, the amount of food eaten is 4 kg and the weight increase is 1 kg, the conversion coefficient is 4·0. In young fish this coefficient is usually low, in older ones high; it is generally in the range 4·8–8·0, depending on the nutritional value (calorie content) of the food.

The living organisms in the sea can all be regarded as links in a food chain, and this is shown in the sketch below

We speak of food competition when two species feed on the same food. For example, in places where the dab occurs in large numbers it may, from the economic viewpoint, become a serious competitor of the more valuable plaice. In this context the cottids are voracious and useless competitors of economically valuable fish.

Distribution of fishes

Off Cape Hatteras the warm Gulf Stream turns away from the coast of North America and continues north-eastwards across the Atlantic as the North Atlantic Drift. Near the American coast this

Phytoplankton: **1** *diatoms* **2** *dinoflagellates*. Zooplankton: **3** *fish eggs* **4** *crab larvae*
5 *crustacean larvae* **6** *pteropods* **7** *copepods* **8** *jellyfishes* **9** *pelagic amphipods* **10**
polychaete worms **11** *cephalopod larvae* **12** *arrow-worms* **13** *fish larvae* **14** *euphausians*

enormous current transports 50 million tons of water a second. On its way across the Atlantic, side currents turn off southwards so that by the time it reaches the area west of Ireland it is only carrying 10 million tons per second. Here the main current divides and sends out branches northwards to south-west Iceland, west Norway and the southern Barents Sea, and south-eastwards to the west coast of France and the Mediterranean Sea. The North Sea also receives water from this warm, North Atlantic current system. The mild winters of the coasts of northern Europe are in fact largely due to the solar energy picked up 2–3 years previously in the area of the Caribbean and Sargasso Seas.

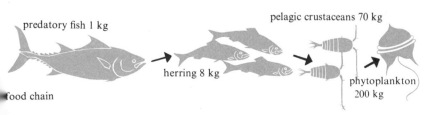

predatory fish 1 kg

herring 8 kg

pelagic crustaceans 70 kg

phytoplankton 200 kg

food chain

Most of our commercial fishes have become adapted to the area of ocean that is climatically influenced by the North Atlantic Drift. This region, known in zoogeography as the boreal region, extends from the Bay of Biscay northwards to the southern Barents Sea. Cod, herring and plaice are among the typical fishes of the boreal region. In addition to the true

cod and also Vahl's eelpout (*Lycodes vahli*) which lives in deep, cold water.

In this book the main distribution of each fish species is shown on a small map. Each species is adapted to a certain temperature range, depth and bottom conditions and is in tough competition with its enemies and other animals for food and for spawning sites.

Gulf Stream and North Atlantic Drift

boreal fishes, the seas off north-western Europe also have many southern species which really belong to the warm-water fauna of the Mediterranean and eastern Atlantic. The northern limit of distribution of these fishes is Ireland and the English Channel. Some are, however, common summer visitors in the North Sea, the Skagerrak and the waters off western Norway, e.g. tunny, grey mullets, sea breams, red mullet, anchovy and John Dory. It is interesting to observe that in the waters off Brittany the southern species invade the habitat of their northern relatives. For example, the pilchard is a southern species whereas the sprat is boreal; they both belong to the herring family and both feed on plankton in coastal waters. They are caught with the same fishing gear and processed in the same way.

In addition to the southern species, the boreal fish fauna also receives northern, arctic-boreal elements, which prefer low temperatures, such as the capelin, the polar

Hydrography

Some knowledge of the chemistry and physics of sea water helps in an understanding of fish biology.

On the average, sea water contains about 35 grams of dissolved salts per litre (salinity = 35 parts per thousand); it is therefore heavier than fresh water. Its specific gravity also depends upon the temperature (warm water is lighter than cold water), and so there is often horizontal stratification with different water masses having different salinities and temperatures. There are many examples of this and a knowledge of this subject is of great importance for sea fisheries. Thus, the warm and therefore light water of the North Atlantic Drift flows in a vast body over the cold water layers of the North Atlantic.

Conditions in the Baltic Sea provide a similar example: there, the salinity of the water is less than in the North Sea owing to the abundant influx of fresh water. The excess water from the Baltic flows through the Sound as a rather brackish and therefore lighter surface current (10–20 m deep), then along the Swedish Kattegat coast and over the top of the more saline Atlantic water approaching in the opposite direction from the North Sea.

Similarly, during winter, the cold brackish water off the Norwegian coast lies in a layer 30–70 m deep over the warmer Atlantic water. At the transition zone between these two layers is the discontinuity layer, (temperature about 5°C) where the Norwegian herring spawn in spring.

Stratification plays an important role in plankton production. During the winter months the surface layers of the North Atlantic cool to a uniform temperature down to a depth of about 500 m. Storms and waves then set up large-scale vertical mixing, and this carries planktonic algae down into deeper water, thus removing them from the sunlight required for their continued existence. In spring, on the other hand, the powerful solar radiation produces a warm upper water layer, 40 m thick, which because of its lower specific gravity lies as a stable covering over the cold water. In this upper layer the algae can receive the sun's rays and the result is an enormous production of plankton. It is during this period of maximum phytoplankton production that the larvae of many of the most important commercial fishes appear. Now and again these larvae

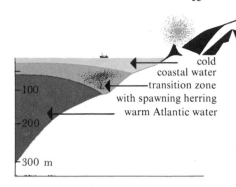

cold
coastal water
transition zone
with spawning herring
warm Atlantic water

hatch too early, and it can happen that considerable numbers of plaice larvae are carried by currents to an area where there is too little plankton.

IDENTIFICATION KEYS:

The key given below is intended to help in the identification of the different fish species. Start at No. 1. Each number on the left side of the key encloses 2–4 different characteristics within a bracket. For each of these characteristics there is, on the right side, either another number or the name of the fish. The species marked with an asterisk are mentioned only in the identification key.

1 { Body eel-like, no paired fins, mouth in the form of a sucking disc .... **Cyclostomes,** p. 31
Body not of that shape **2**

2 { No gill covers, 5–7 gill slits .... **Sharks and rays,** Key I, below

Gill covers present **3**

3 { Lateral line forming a characteristic pattern on the head .... **Chimaera,** p. 59
Without such a pattern.......................... **Bony fishes,** Key II, p. 23

Key I Sharks and rays

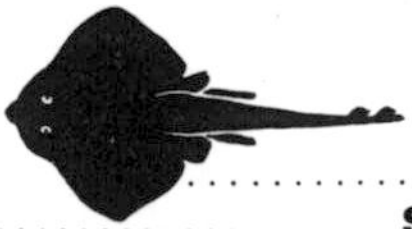

1 { Body disc-shaped, gill openings ventral .... **Rays 2**
Gill slits lateral, in front of pectoral fins .... **Sharks 12**

2 { Tail whip-like, armed with a spine **3**
Tail with two small dorsal fins **4**

3 { **Eagle ray,** *Myliobatis aquila*, p. 58 and .... **Sting ray,** p. 59

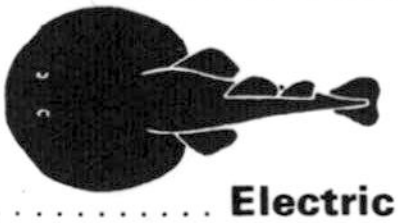

4 { Body almost circular, skin without thorns................ **Electric rays,** p. 51
Body broad **5**

5 { Snout obtuse-angled **6**
Snout rectangular or acute-angled **9**

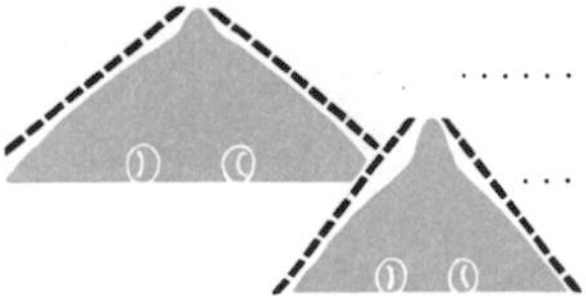

6 — Large dorsal spines with smooth basal plates .... **Thornback ray,** p. 53

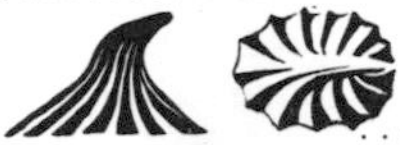

Dorsal spines, when present, with ribbed basal plates **7**

7 — Front edge of body disc very convex .... **Fylla's ray,** p. 53

Front edge only slightly convex or straight **8**

Up to 16 large spines in a longitudinal row on the back .... **Starry ray,** p. 53

Spines on back small or absent: the following 6 species occur from the Mediterranean to the English Channel:

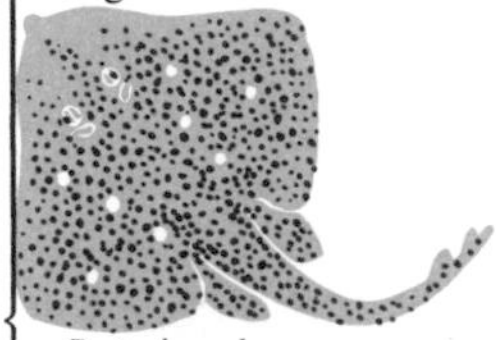

8

Raja brachyura
Blonde ray*

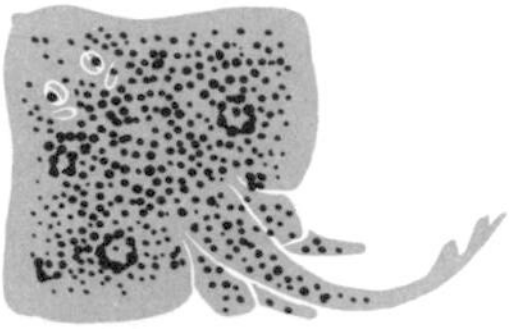

Raja montagui
Spotted ray*

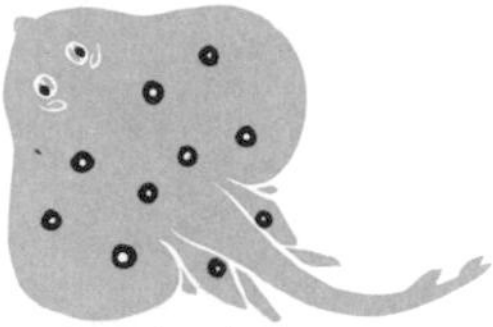

Raja circularis
Sandy ray*

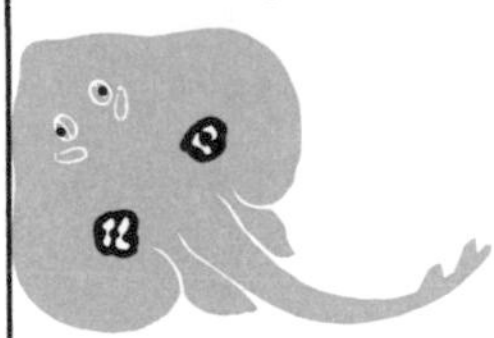

Raja naevus
Cuckoo ray*

Raja undulata
Undulate ray*

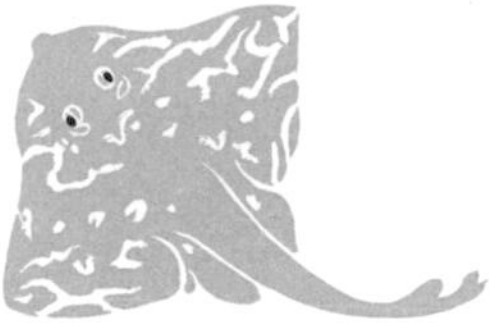

Raja microocellata
Painted ray*

9 — Underside of body uniform white; spines on back and tail **10**

Underside dark or spotted; spines only on tail, and possibly near eyes **11**

10 — Dorsal side of tail with a central row of spines .... **Pale ray,** p. 57

Dorsal side of tail without a central row of spines .... **Shagreen ray,** p. 57

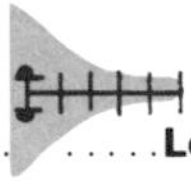

11 — Snout 5–6 times the distance between eyes .... **Long-nose skate,** p. 57

Snout *c.* 3 times the distance between eyes .... **Skate,** p. 55

12 — Six gill slits, only one dorsal fin **13**

Five gill slits, two dorsal fins **14**

13 — Tail length *c.* $\frac{1}{3}$ the total length .... **Six-gilled shark,*** *Hexanchus griseus*

Tail not strikingly elongated .... **Frilled shark,*** *Chlamydoselachus anguineus*

14 Body flattened, mouth terminal .... **Monkfish,** p. 51

Body not that shape **15**

15 With one spine in front of each dorsal fin **16**

Without spines in front of dorsal fins................................ **17**

16 First dorsal fin smaller than second .... **Velvet belly,** p. 47

Caudal fin with broad lobes........................ *Centrophorus squamosus*

Caudal fin without lobes .... **Spur-dog,** p. 45

17 With an anal fin............................... ....**18**

Without an anal fin............................ **Greenland shark,** p. 49

18 First dorsal fin behind ventral fins ....

Lesser spotted dogfish, p. 46 and **Black-mouthed dogfish,** p. 46

First dorsal fin in front of ventrals **19**

19 Caudal fin about as long as body ....

Thresher, p. 41

Caudal fin not strikingly elongated................................... **20**

20 Gill slits very long ....

Basking shark, p. 39

Gill slits small **21**

21 Dorsal and ventral constriction of caudal peduncle .... **Blue shark,** p. 42

Without such constriction **22**

22 Caudal fin shaped like halfmoon **23**

Caudal fin not like halfmoon **24**

23 Rear edge of pectoral fins lying forward of 1st dorsal fin; teeth one-pointed .... **Mako,** * *Isurus oxyrinchus*

Rear edge of pectoral fins lying below 1st dorsal fin; teeth three-pointed .... **Porbeagle,** p. 37

24 The two dorsal fins almost equal in size ...... **Smooth hound,** p. 41

Second dorsal fin distinctly smaller .... **Tope,** p. 41

Key II Bony fishes

The following 10 bony fishes have such a typical appearance that they can be immediately identified by their shape:

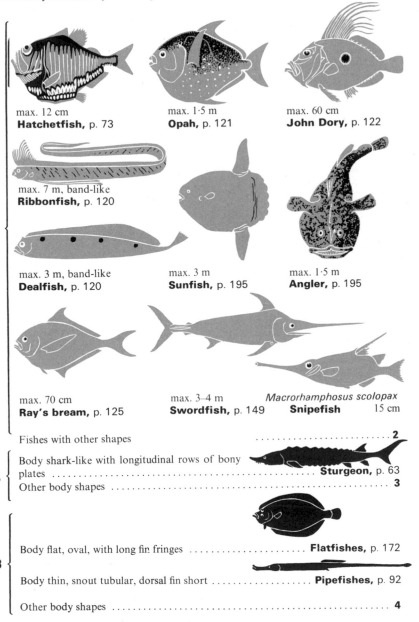

max. 12 cm
Hatchetfish, p. 73

max. 1·5 m
Opah, p. 121

max. 60 cm
John Dory, p. 122

max. 7 m, band-like
Ribbonfish, p. 120

max. 3 m, band-like
Dealfish, p. 120

max. 3 m
Sunfish, p. 195

max. 1·5 m
Angler, p. 195

max. 70 cm
Ray's bream, p. 125

max. 3–4 m
Swordfish, p. 149

Macrorhamphosus scolopax
Snipefish   15 cm

1

Fishes with other shapes **2**

2

Body shark-like with longitudinal rows of bony plates .... **Sturgeon,** p. 63

Other body shapes **3**

3

Body flat, oval, with long fin fringes .... **Flatfishes,** p. 172

Body thin, snout tubular, dorsal fin short .... **Pipefishes,** p. 92

Other body shapes **4**

24

4 {
Snout elongated and beak-like; unpaired fins lying far back **5**

Snout with 2–4 barbels .... **Rocklings,** p. 119
Different characters **6**

5 {
With finlets behind dorsal and anal fins .... **Garfish,** p. 89
Without finlets .... **Skipper,** p. 90

6 {
With two dorsal fins, and finlets on caudal peduncle .... **Mackerel,** p. 139
Without these characters **7**

7 {
With a few isolated, movable spines in front of dorsal fin .... **Sticklebacks,** p. 171
Without such spines **8**

8 {
With one short, soft-rayed dorsal fin; without lateral line .... **Herring,** p. 64

With one short, soft-rayed dorsal fin and one small ray-less adipose fin **9**
Without these characters **13**

9 {
With light organs along belly .... **Sheppy argentine,** p. 73
Without light organs **10**

10 {
Ventral fins below rear edge of dorsal fin; eyes very large .... **Lesser and larger argentines,** p. 81

Ventral fins below the middle or front part of dorsal fin **11**

11 {
Anal fin somewhat longer than dorsal fin; body slender **12**

Anal fin somewhat shorter than dorsal fin ...... **Salmon,** p. 75 and **trout,** p. 79

12 {
At most 80 scales in a longitudinal row .... **Smelt,** p. 81
At least 150 scales in a longitudinal row .... **Capelin,** p. 81

13 {
Without clearly defined caudal fin **14**
With distinct caudal fin **15**

4 With a chin barbel; tail long and thin, often broken off ....**Grenadier,** p. 95

Without these characters **15**

5 Ventral fins small; an indentation at rear end of dorsal fin .... **Eelpout,** p. 155

Ventral fins small; dorsal fin without indentation .... **Vahl's eelpout,** p. 155

Without ventral fins; small gill opening near pectoral fin base .... **Eel,** p. 83

6 Small, slender fish with pointed snouts and silvery sides; no ventral fins .... **Sand-eels,** p. 133

Without these characters **17**

7 Ventral fins more or less fused, forming a saucer or funnel; two dorsal fins; rarely over 10 cm long **18**

Ventral fins more or less modified to form suction disc **24**

Ventral fins, if present, not fused **25**

8 Body transparent ....**Crystal goby** and **Transparent goby,** p. 159

Body not transparent **19**

9 Caudal peduncle significantly shorter than 2nd dorsal fin base **20**

Caudal peduncle as long as 2nd dorsal fin base **21**

0 50–58 scales in a longitudinal row; first 4 rays in 1st dorsal fin equal in length ...... **Rock goby,** see under **black goby,** p. 156

35–42 scales in a longitudinal row; 4th ray in 1st dorsal fin elongated and curved backwards .... **Black goby,** p. 156

25–30 scales in a longitudinal row; caudal fin pointed .... **Fries's goby,** see under **black goby,** p. 156

1 1st dorsal fin with 7–8 spiny rays; a large black spot on tail base .... **Two-spot goby,** p. 157

1st dorsal fin with 5–6 spiny rays **22**

26

22
- 2nd spiny ray of dorsal fin elongated .... **Jeffreys's goby,** *Buenia jeffreysi*
- 2nd spiny ray not elongated **23**

23
- 61–73 scales in longitudinal row . . . . **Sand goby,** p. 159
- 42–52 scales in longitudinal row . . . . **Common goby,** see under **painted goby,** p. 158
- 35–41 scales in longitudinal row . . . . **Painted goby,** p. 158

24
- Body thick-set, armed with bony denticles . . . **Lumpsucker,** p. 168
- Small fishes with long dorsal and anal fins . . . . **Sea snails,** p. 169
- Small fishes with divided suction disc and a dark spot behind the pectoral fin . . . . **Two-spotted clingfish** *Diplecogaster bimaculata*

25
- 1st dorsal fin very small (only 3 fin rays); one barbel on chin; lateral line indistinct; not longer than 20 cm; blackish-brown . . . .**Tadpole-fish,** p. 113
- Only one dorsal fin; one barbel on chin; lateral line distinct; unpaired fins bordered by black band with white edge . . . . **Torsk,** p. 117
- Other characters **26**

26
- With two separate dorsal fins **27**
- With only one dorsal fin **36**

27
- 1st dorsal fin with spiny rays **29**
- 1st dorsal fin with branched soft rays **28**

28
- No barbel on chin; anal and 2nd dorsal fins indented behind the middle . . . . **Hake,** p. 117
- One barbel on chin; anal and 2nd dorsal fins without indentation . . . . **Ling,** p. 114
- One barbel on chin; ventral fins long and filamentous. . . . . **Greater forkbeard,** p. 113

29
- Lower part of pectoral fins with three free-moving fin rays . . . . **Gurnards,** p. 162
- Pectorals without free rays **30**

Distance between the 2 dorsal fins greater than the height of the 1st dorsal fin **31**

Dorsal fins close together or with only a small distance between them **32**

With two large chin barbels . . . . **Red mullet,** p. 125

1st dorsal fin with thin spiny rays; an iridescent line along each side . . . . **Sand-smelt,** p. 137

Dorsal fins widely separated, first having 4 spiny rays; 7–8 dark longitudinal stripes . . . . **Grey mullets,** p. 138

1st dorsal fin significantly shorter than the 2nd . . . **33**

The 2 dorsal fins almost equal in length **35**

Caudal fin deeply forked; lateral line with strikingly large, plate-like scales . . . . **Scad,** p. 123

Caudal fin not deeply forked; lateral line without large scales **34**

Anal fin short; 2nd dorsal fin twice as long as the 1st; large scales on head and body . . . . **Meagre,** p. 125

Anal fin long; 2nd dorsal fin 4–5 times as long as the 1st, with more than 20 rays. Gill cover with a large, backward-directed spine . . . . **Greater weever,** p. 135

Anal fin long; 2nd dorsal fin 3 times as long as the 1st with a maximum of 10 rays, in males the rays of the first dorsal fin are much elongated . . . . **Dragonets,** p. 137

Body armoured with bony plates; snout with 2 pointed spines; barbels on underside of head . . . . **Pogge,** p. 167

Body without scales; front of gill cover with 1 or more spines . . . . **Bullheads,** p. 164

Body with scales; front gill cover with teeth; anal fin with 3 spiny rays . . . . **Bass,** p. 123

Anal fin longer than dorsal fin. Colour reddish . . . . **Beryx,** p. 120

Anal fin shorter than dorsal fin **37**

With clearly visible scales; normal body shape **38**

Without or with only small, smooth scales. 'Wolf-fish body' **41**

38
Gill cover armed with spines; colour reddish . . . . **Redfish,** p. 161

Gill cover with a prominent ridge . . . . **Wreckfish,*** *Polyprion americanus*
Gill cover without spines **39**

39
Front part of dorsal fin with spiny rays **40**

Dorsal fin without spiny rays . . . . **Blackfish,*** *Centrolophus niger*

40
Pectoral fins pointed, caudal fin forked . . . . **Sea breams,** p. 126

Pectoral fins rounded, caudal fin edge straight.
Brightly coloured fishes . . . . **Wrasses,** p. 128

41
With very powerful teeth; no ventral fins. Large
fish from depths of 20–600 m **42**
Teeth small; ventral fins present but may be very
small. Small fish from shallow water **43**

42
With dark transverse bars . . . . **Catfish,** p. 153
Brownish with distinct spots . . . . **Spotted catfish,** p. 153
Dark bluish, with indistinct spots . . . . **Jelly cat,** p. 153

43
Distance between mouth and start of anal fin
about $\frac{1}{3}$ total length . . . . **Snake blenny,** p. 151
Distance between mouth and start of anal fin
about $\frac{1}{2}$ total length **44**

44
Body elongated with dark spots along dorsal fin
base . . . . **Butterfish,** p. 151

Dorsal fin with one conspicuous dark spot . . . . **Butterfly blenny,** p. 151

Dorsal fin distinctly concave in the middle; 2
tentacles above eyes . . . . **Montagu's blenny,** p. 151

Dorsal fin slightly concave in the middle; 2
tentacles above eyes . . . . **Tompot blenny,** p. 151

Dorsal fin distinctly concave in the middle;
without tentacles . . . . **Shanny,** p. 151

Dorsal fin without indentation; 2 pairs of tentacles
above eyes . . . . **Yarrell's blenny,** p. 151

ILLUSTRATIONS AND DESCRIPTIONS

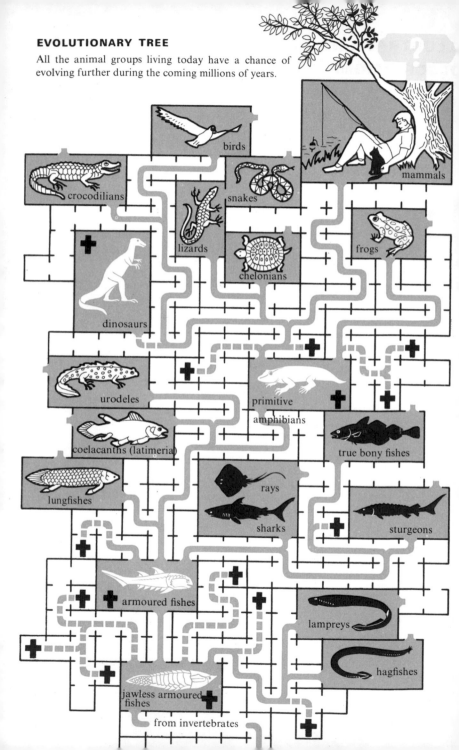

EVOLUTIONARY TREE

All the animal groups living today have a chance of evolving further during the coming millions of years.

birds

mammals

crocodilians

snakes

lizards

frogs

chelonians

dinosaurs

urodeles

primitive amphibians

coelacanths (latimeria)

true bony fishes

lungfishes

rays

sharks

sturgeons

armoured fishes

lampreys

hagfishes

jawless armoured fishes

from invertebrates

CYCLOSTOMES

Cyclostomata

The cyclostomes (lampreys and hagfishes) are the most primitive of all living vertebrates. The word cyclostomes refers to their circular, funnel-shaped, sucking mouth armed with horny teeth. The cyclostomes are not closely related to the cartilaginous fishes (selachians) or to the bony fishes (see p. 30); in contrast to these they have neither jaws nor paired fins. Their eel-like body is covered with a scaleless, shiny skin, and their skeleton is cartilaginous and poorly developed.

The structure of their gill apparatus is best understood by looking at a longitudinal section of the front end of the animal. On each side of the fore-gut there are seven gill pouches, which either communicate directly with the body surface (as in lampreys), or they open on each side into a common tube, which carries away the water used in respiration (hagfishes). The lampreys can either take in water through the mouth or they can suck it in and expel it through the gill openings. The hagfishes, on the other hand, suck in water through the unpaired nasal opening and expel it through the gill tube. Neither lampreys nor hagfishes possess a swimbladder.

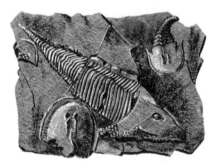

The cyclostomes have an evolutionary history of some 400–500 million years. They split off very early on from the main line of the true fishes. Their ancestors, the peculiar jawless armoured fishes (Ostracoderms) known as fossils from the Devonian period, had a strong bony armour and apparently lived primarily in fresh waters. The 45 existing species of cyclostomes may be regarded as the last degenerate descendants of these armoured fishes.

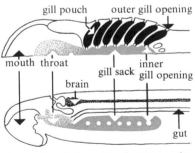

side and dorsal view of the front part of a lamprey

1. Sea lamprey

Petromyzon marinus L.

Distinctive features: Mouth disc with numerous circular rows of horny teeth (fig. 1b).

Average length 60–75 cm, maximum 100 cm. Feeds by rasping the skin of fishes and sucking the blood; they are often found attached by the sucking mouth to cod, herring, mackerel and sharks. They rasp a hole in the victim's skin and secrete into the wound a substance that dissolves the tissues and prevents coagulation of the blood. They enter the rivers in autumn or early spring and spawn on stony bottoms in February-June. They cease to feed while moving up the rivers. The male clears the spawning site of stones with his mouth. During mating the female adheres by suction to a stone and the male coils around her. In this process, which is repeated every five minutes, the female lays a total of up to about 200,000 to 240,000 eggs, each 1 mm across, and these are fertilised by the male. The sand stirred up during mating sticks to the eggs and brings them down to the bottom. The parents cover them with stones and die shortly after mating. The eggs hatch in 1–2 weeks. The larvae or ammocoetes are very unlike the adults; for 2–5 years they live like worms in burrows of mucus in the mud. They only metamorphose into the fully-formed lamprey when they are 15–20 cm long and then migrate into the sea. During the winter months the rich, fatty flesh of lampreys is very well-flavoured, but they have no commercial importance.

2. River lamprey

Lampetra fluviatilis (L.)

Distinctive features: Mouth disc with only one row of horny teeth (fig. 2b).

Males reach a length of 31–32 cm, females 32–34, rarely 40 cm. Similar in general habits and breeding to the sea lamprey. As they move up the rivers to spawn the gut starts to regress, and the dorsal fins enlarge. The female lays 4,000–40,000 eggs, and both adults die after spawning. The larval stage lasts 4–5 years. Metamorphosis to the adult form takes place at a length of 9–15 cm, and they migrate into the sea where they remain for 1–2 years.

During their passage upstream river lampreys are caught in traps and purse-nets and are marketed in salted, smoked or marinated form, but they are still of little economic importance.

3. Hagfish

Myxine glutinosa L.

Distinctive features: Eel-like body, with 4 barbels near the mouth and 4 at the nostrils. Skin naked and slimy. A small fringe of fin around the tail only. Blind.

Males reach a length of 25–30 cm, females 30–42 cm. These are nocturnal animals which live on soft bottoms at depths of 20–800 m. They become sexually mature at a length of 25–28 cm and evidently breed the whole year round in deep water. The female lays 20–30 oval eggs (length 17–25 mm), each surrounded by a horny shell with hooked filaments at each end. The eggs probably take several weeks to develop. Adult hagfishes feed on bottom-living animals, but they also bore into and eat fish caught on lines, and in some places they may therefore do considerable damage to long-line fisheries. Hagfishes have a highly developed sense of smell, and they seem to prefer areas with currents that can convey the scent of food. Of no economic value.

1. SEA LAMPREY

Petromyzon marinus

a 35 cm **b** head from below

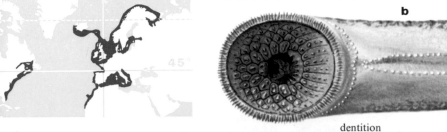

dentition

2. RIVER LAMPREY

Lampetra fluviatilis

a 28 cm
b head from below

dentition

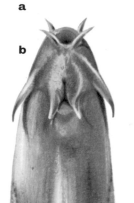

3. HAGFISH

Myxine glutinosa

a 35 cm
b head from below
c egg, 22 mm
d adhering eggs from the sea bottom

CARTILAGINOUS FISHES

Chondrichthyes

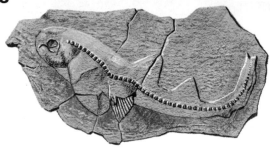

This group contains the sharks, dogfishes, rays, skates and the peculiar rabbitfishes. It is thought that they have been evolved from freshwater or brackish-water forms which subsequently went over to life in the sea. A large number of long-extinct cartilaginous fishes are known as fossils. The *c.* 500 living species are really only the remnants of a group which held a dominant position among the fishes about 250 million years ago in the Carboniferous period.

Almost all the cartilaginous fishes have a long snout, but the transverse mouth is positioned quite far back on the underside of the head.

A characteristic feature of the sharks and rays is that, like the cyclostomes, they have external gill openings, without gill covers, whereas in the related rabbitfishes, and also in the bony fishes, the delicate gills are protected by gill covers.

Sharks have 5–7 gill openings, rays always only 5. In addition, some sharks and all the rays possess a pair of openings, known as spiracles, behind the eyes. These are particularly well developed in those species that live on the bottom. When lying half buried in the bottom, waiting for prey, a ray sucks water for respiration in through the spiracles and this prevents the gills from being covered by sand.

Other characters of these fishes are the stiff, fleshy fins which cannot be folded like those of bony fishes. The caudal fin is asymmetrical, the upper lobe being better

developed than the lower lobe. The tall triangular dorsal fin and the upper lobe of the caudal fin of sharks often project above the water surface.

The sharks and rays have no true scales, but dermal denticles which are covered with a layer of hard enamel. These small, closely packed structures, with their points facing backwards give shark skin a roughness akin to that of sandpaper; the skin has, in fact, been used as an abrasive.

In the rays these dermal denticles are modified to form large thorns which are

arranged either far apart on the body surface or in irregular rows. The skin of adult rabbitfishes is naked.

The skeleton consists exclusively of cartilage; only the cranium and the vertebral column may be strengthened by some deposition of calcium salts. True bony tissue is never present.

The jaws are usually heavily armed with teeth, arranged in several rows, one behind the other. The foremost teeth are worn away first and are replaced by the next series and so on.

In the sharks the teeth are either pointed, needle-like and used for gripping or triangular, razor-sharp and used for cutting. The rays and also a few shark species have flat, stumpy teeth arranged like

paving, and these are adapted for crushing snails and bivalves.

The alimentary canal is short, but internally it has a spiral fold, the spiral valve, which slows down the passage of the food and increases the area of absorption.

Sharks and rays have no swimbladder. To some extent the very large oily liver helps buoyancy.

In contrast to the majority of bony fishes which release their eggs and sperm into the open water, the sharks and rays have a form of copulation and internal fertilisation. In the male the rear ventral fin rays are modified as clasping organs which serve in gripping the female during copulation. Most sharks and many rays are viviparous, that is, the young are born alive as miniature replicas of the parents. Other species lay eggs which are enclosed in a large, more or less translucent horny capsule which has filamentous outgrowths that help to fasten the eggs to seaweeds or stones. The eggs and young are relatively large, the number of offspring correspondingly small. For instance, the

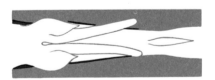

female Porbeagle produces only 1–4 young at a time, but these are *c.* 60 cm long at birth.

Some shark and ray species occur in tropical rivers, but most members of the group are adapted for life in the sea. The two largest species are the whale shark (15 m) and the basking shark (12 m), both peaceful consumers of plankton like the whalebone whales.

The pelagic manta rays with a 'wing span' of up to 6 m are the largest of the rays.

Some of the sharks and rays are of economic importance. Although the flesh of the different species is not in much demand in Europe and North America it

is quite important in China, Japan and Pakistan where, for example, dried shark's fin is made into tasty soups. The fins are also used as a raw material in the manu-

facture of glue. Shark skin is tanned and worked up as ornamental leather (shagreen). The oil from the liver is extracted for certain technical purposes and is increasingly used in the production of vitamin preparations.

SHARKS

Pleurotremata

With the exception of the monkfish which is broad and flat like a ray, all the sharks have a torpedo-shaped body with a triangular cross section.

None of the different shark species in the North Atlantic is dangerous to man. About 99% of all the stories about the danger of sharks are grossly exaggerated.

Many of the injuries and accidents that occur among bathers in tropical seas are not due to the attacks of 'man-eating' sharks but are caused by barracudas, which are large pike-like fishes which sometimes come into shallow coastal waters.

The few shark species which may be dangerous to man (blue shark, white shark) must share their bad reputation with the barracuda and a few other bony fishes.

The majority of sharks lead a predatory life and feed mainly on fish. A few, however, appear to prefer a more mixed diet. Their stomachs must, indeed, be very tough if one is to judge from the varied assortment found in them over the course of many years.

It is very difficult to determine the exact age of a shark, but tagging experiments have shown that growth is slow and that many sharks live for more than 20 years.

4. Porbeagle

Lamna nasus (Bonnaterre)

Average length 1·5–3 m, maximum *c.* 3·5 m. Weight 150–200 kg. Usually lives in the upper waters and is only rarely caught in depths below 150 m. Gravid females can be found throughout the year. The embryos lie free in the uterus; as soon as they have consumed their own yolk mass, and are about 6 cm long, they start to consume any unfertilised eggs, and this causes their stomach to swell. The newly born young are *c.* 60 cm long. Litter size: 1–4.

Nothing is known about their growth and longevity. The females are sexually mature at a length of 1·5 m.

The porbeagle is a fast and efficient swimmer. It can often be observed hunting herring and mackerel close to the surface. It will also hunt spur-dogs, cod, flatfishes and squids. It does considerable damage to fisheries by raiding and tearing the nets. Porbeagles are caught on strong shark hooks, using a herring or a mackerel as bait. Sometimes a few may be taken accidentally in herring nets. Porbeagles are mainly caught in the northern North Sea and off the Orkney and Shetland Islands. In winter they appear to move further south, and possibly also into deeper water. In spite of its frightening appearance it is not dangerous to man.

These sharks are mainly hunted off Norway whence the flesh is exported to other countries including Germany, where it is marketed under various names. The ammoniacal smell of the flesh disappears on cooking, and the flavour resembles that of veal.

The liver, which may weigh up to 50 kg, yields a valuable oil, and the skin can be made into leather.

The mako, a relative from the warmer parts of the Atlantic, is occasionally caught by sea anglers off the coast of Cornwall.

4. PORBEAGLE

Lamna nasus

a Male, *c.* 3·5 m **b** jaws
c principal method of capture

b

c shark hook

5. Basking shark

Cetorhinus maximus (Gunnerus)

Maximum length 12 m, weight 3,500–4,000 kg. Like the whalebone whales, this shark feeds on plankton. The gill arches carry a large number of long, slender horny gill rakers which act as a filter. As the sharks swim along with open mouth, the water flows in and the plankton it contains is caught on this filter. The filtered water is then expelled through the enormously enlarged gill slits. At a swimming speed of 2 knots the basking shark can in this way filter the plankton out of *c.* 1,500 tons of water in one hour.

Basking sharks become sexually mature when about 7 m long and 2–4 years old. The gestation period is 2 years, and the female gives birth to one, or at the most two young, which are 1·5 m long.

These sharks live solitarily or in shoals of up to 50–250 individuals. Their main centre of distribution is south of Iceland. They occur as summer visitors in the waters off the Hebrides and Orkney. From there they move into the northern North Sea and off western Norway. In the autumn they turn round and in November probably move down into deeper water. During the winter months the gill rakers are resorbed and are only re-formed again in February, so it can be assumed that these sharks do not feed during the cold part of the year when there is, at any rate, little plankton.

Since basking sharks feed on plankton they cannot be caught on a hook, but they are occasionally harpooned by whale-catchers. The gigantic liver of this shark weighs up to 500–700 kg, that is about 25% of the total body weight, and may yield 6–15 hectolitres of oil. These sharks grow slowly and have a low rate of reproduction and so the population is threatened by overfishing.

Stranded, partly skeletonised basking sharks were at one time taken to be 'sea serpents'.

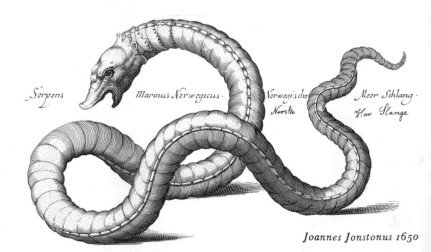

Serpens   *Marinus Norwegicus.*   *Norwegische*   *Meer Schlang.*
Norske   *Hav Slange*

Joannes Jonstonus 1650

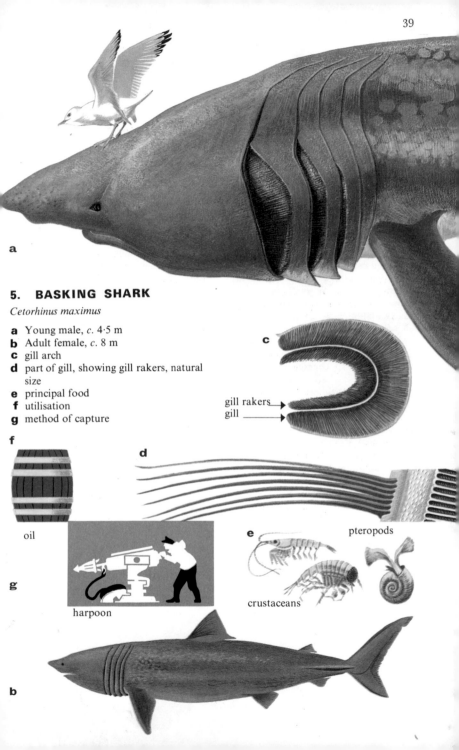

5. BASKING SHARK

Cetorhinus maximus

a Young male, *c.* 4·5 m
b Adult female, *c.* 8 m
c gill arch
d part of gill, showing gill rakers, natural size
e principal food
f utilisation
g method of capture

gill rakers
gill

oil

harpoon

pteropods

crustaceans

6. Thresher

Alopias vulpinus (Bonnaterre)

Characteristics: Extraordinarily long upper lobe to the caudal fin.

The colour of the upperside varies from brown to slate-grey or almost completely black.

Threshers reach a length of up to 6 m and a weight of about 500 kg. They undertake extensive migrations, during which they swim just beneath the surface of the sea. In later summer they are regularly seen, albeit in small numbers, in the waters north of Ireland. They become sexually mature at a length of *c.* 4 m; nothing is known about the period of gestation. The young (usually 2–4) are 1·2–1·5 m long at birth, and even then they have the long tail characteristic of the species.

Threshers feed almost exclusively on pelagic shoaling fishes, particularly mackerel and herring. They have often been seen swimming in ever-decreasing circles around a shoal of fish, their large tail fin threshing the water. In this way they concentrate their victims before moving in for the kill.

Threshers are of no economic importance, although from time to time a few are accidentally caught in herring nets. Occasionally they do some damage to drift nets. They are not dangerous to man.

7. Smooth hound

Mustelus mustelus (L.)

Characteristics: Teeth like paving stones, as in the rays. The two dorsal fins are almost equal in size.

There are two related species in European waters: *M. mustelus* and *M. asterias,* the latter having pale spots on the sides of the body.

Maximum length 2 m. Gravid females can be found at all times of the year. Litter size: 10–20, rarely more.

Smooth hounds live in coastal waters in depths of 20–100 m, and feed on lobsters, crawfish, crabs, molluscs and small bottom-living fishes.

They are of little economic importance.

8. Tope

Galeorhinus galeus (L.)

Characteristics: Without a spine in front of either dorsal fin. First dorsal fin 2–3 times as large as the second. Eyes with a nictitating membrane at the front of the lower eyelid. The triangular teeth have a sharp point and are serrated on the hind side. Maximum length 2 m.

Tope live close to the bottom in depths of 40–100 m and feed mainly on bottom-living fishes. They breed in June-September and the female produces 20–40 young, which are *c.* 40 cm long at birth.

Of no economic importance.

Smooth hound

Tope

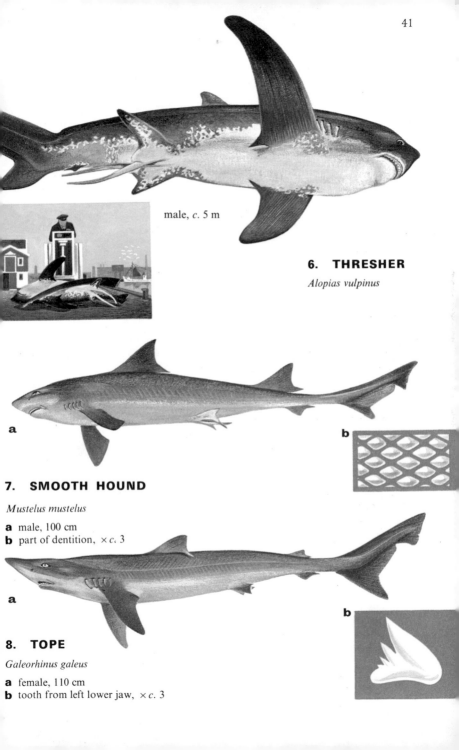

male, *c.* 5 m

6. THRESHER
Alopias vulpinus

7. SMOOTH HOUND

Mustelus mustelus

a male, 100 cm
b part of dentition, × *c.* 3

8. TOPE

Galeorhinus galeus

a female, 110 cm
b tooth from left lower jaw, × *c.* 3

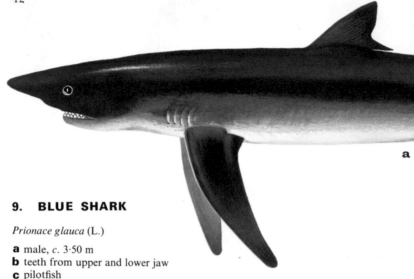

a

9. BLUE SHARK

Prionace glauca (L.)

a male, *c.* 3·50 m
b teeth from upper and lower jaw
c pilotfish

Characteristics: Without a spine in front of either dorsal fin. Eyes with a nictitating membrane. A transverse constriction at the base of the caudal fin. Unlike the porbeagle, the caudal peduncle has no lateral keels. Each tooth has only one point and serrated edges. Spiracles absent. Seldom over 4 m.

Blue sharks live in the open ocean and often undertake long migrations. They become sexually mature when *c.* 2·5 m long. The embryos are nourished within the mother's body through a placental attachment to her uterus wall.

Litter size: 25–50. The new-born young are 50–60 cm long. Nothing is known about the period of mating.

b

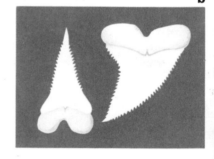

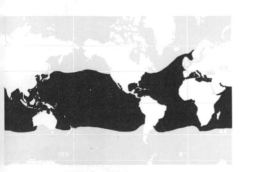

Blue sharks feed principally on shoaling fishes, particularly mackerel and herring, but occasionally they also attack cod, spur-dogs and squids.

They occur as regular but not very abundant visitors in the northern part of the North Sea.

Although regarded as one of the 'man-eating' sharks, the danger is usually much exaggerated.

Of no economic value in Europe where the flesh is not appreciated. In Japan, on the other hand, this species is caught in considerable numbers, using shark hooks.

Pilotfish often accompany the large sharks. They feed on scraps from the shark's meals. It is not true that they lead the shark to its prey.

c

de Bry

Most of the severe injuries caused by sharks are the result of attacks by tiger sharks and white sharks.

10. Spur-dog

Squalus acanthias (L.)

In front of each dorsal fin there is a powerful spine, with a small venom gland in a furrow on its dorsal side. First dorsal fin larger than the second. No anal fin. A closely related form extends from the south into Irish waters and can be distinguished by its plain, unspotted brownish colour and by its eyes which are twice as large as those of the present species.

Spur-dogs reach a length of 1 m, rarely 1·2 m, and a maximum weight of 10 kg. They live close to the bottom in shallow water and also down to depths of *c.* 400 m.

This is the most abundant shark species in the North Atlantic, and on muddy bottoms with a water temperature of 6–15°C they sometimes live in shoals numbering thousands.

They undertake extensive migrations, covering long distances every day. In summer they are particularly numerous off the Shetland Islands and in winter in the coastal waters off Norway, but they are rare off Greenland.

The female has a gestation period of 18–22 months. An elongated, translucent horny capsule containing 1–6 eggs is formed in each oviduct. This common covering disappears in the course of further development, so in effect the young hatch within the mother's body, where they then lie free in the oviduct. The female usually produces 4–8 young, which are 20–33 cm long at birth. Their subsequent growth is slow. At sexual maturity the males are 60–80 cm long, the females 75–90 cm. Longevity: 20–24 years, calculated from the number of growth lines in the dorsal spines.

Spur-dogs feed on cod, herring, crustaceans and other invertebrates. They often damage fishing gear and nets.

In winter they are caught off Norway on hooks and also in trawls; thousands of tons are landed in Europe.

After capture these fish are skinned and decapitated. The dorsal and ventral parts are exported from Norway to Britain and Germany, either on ice or deep-frozen. In some countries the eggs are also eaten. The liver is used in the preparation of an oil rich in vitamins.

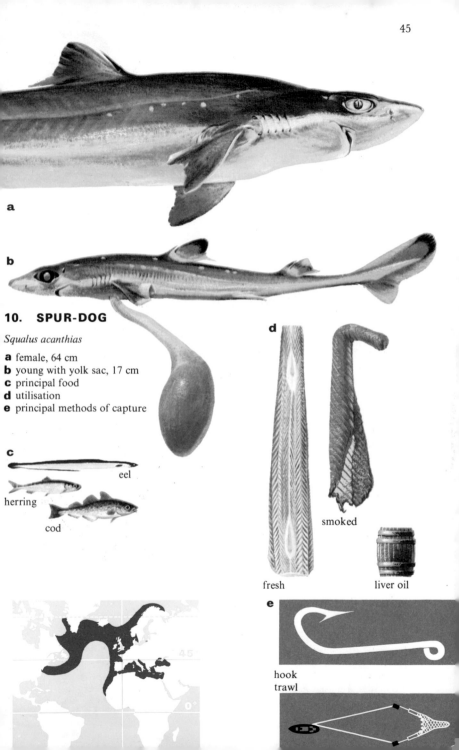

10. SPUR-DOG

Squalus acanthias

a female, 64 cm
b young with yolk sac, 17 cm
c principal food
d utilisation
e principal methods of capture

a

b

c

eel

herring

cod

d

fresh

smoked

liver oil

e

hook
trawl

11. Velvet belly

Etmopterus spinax (L.)

With a powerful spine in front of each dorsal fin. The second dorsal fin is larger than the first. The velvety appearance of the skin is particularly striking. The greenish iridescence of the belly is produced by small light organs embedded in the skin.

Rarely over 45 cm in length, these fish occur in the eastern North Atlantic and Mediterranean, in depths of 75–700 m. In summer the female produces 10–14 young, each *c.* 10 cm long.

The velvet belly feeds on fishes, squids

and prawns. It is of no economic importance, but may do damage to fisheries by tearing cod and halibut off the hooks.

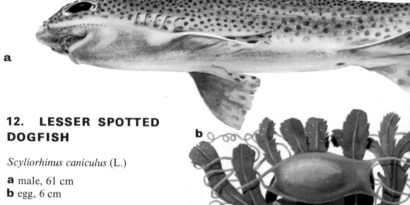

a

12. LESSER SPOTTED DOGFISH

Scyliorhinus caniculus (L.)

a male, 61 cm
b egg, 6 cm

The rear ends of the ventral fins are pointed and produced. Length 60–80 cm, maximum 100 cm. Frequents sand banks with algal growth in depths of 10–85 m. Dogfish become active at night, when they hunt for small fishes, crustaceans and molluscs.

In spring the female lays 18–20 egg capsules (*c.* 6 cm long) which become attached to rocks and seaweeds. These hatch in 8–10 months.

The more stoutly built nursehound or larger spotted dogfish (*S. stellaris*) has rounded rear edges to the ventral fins; it only occurs rather uncommonly north of the western English Channel.

b

eggs on sea

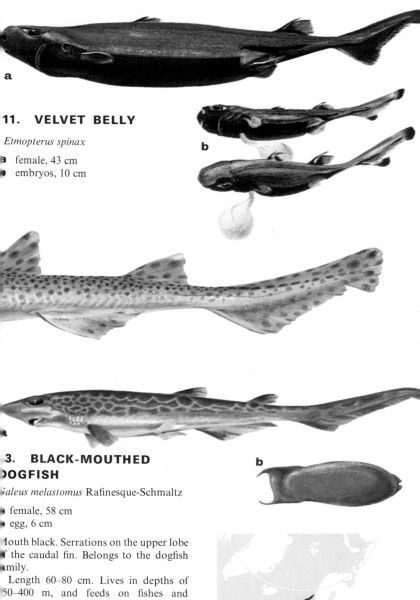

11. VELVET BELLY

Etmopterus spinax

a female, 43 cm
b embryos, 10 cm

3. BLACK-MOUTHED DOGFISH

Galeus melastomus Rafinesque-Schmaltz

a female, 58 cm
b egg, 6 cm

Mouth black. Serrations on the upper lobe
of the caudal fin. Belongs to the dogfish
family.

Length 60–80 cm. Lives in depths of
50–400 m, and feeds on fishes and
crustaceans. The females become sexually
mature at a length of *c.* 70 cm, and they
lay egg capsules (6 cm long) in spring.
Sometimes caught in the trawl, but of no
value.

Greenland Shark

Somniosus microcephalus (Bloch and Schneider)

Average length 3–4 m, maximum *c*. 8 m. This is an arctic, deep-sea species usually found at depths of 200–600 m, particularly in waters over muddy ground, at a temperature of 0–7°C. Occasionally it moves far outside its distribution range, and now and again it even reaches the coasts of France.

The young are probably born in the winter; they are 40–70 cm long at birth. Their slow rate of growth is shown by a specimen caught and marked off Greenland when it was 262 cm long. It was recaptured some 16 years later and its length had only increased by 8 cm. Large specimens must therefore be a great age.

Greenland sharks are omnivorous, although they appear to prefer cod and halibut. They often tear hooked fish or bait off long lines and may therefore damage the fisheries.

Like most sharks they have an extraordinarily well-developed sense of smell, which quickly leads them to prey. The stomach has often been found to contain a seal, and on one occasion an entire reindeer. Vision, on the other hand, is poor, and the cornea of the eye is often destroyed by a species of parasitic crustacean.

When caught on a hook, a Greenland shark's behaviour is completely indifferent, for it allows itself to be hauled on board without putting up any resistance. This behaviour is reflected in the generic name *somniosus* (sleepy). It is caught on a large hook, baited with putrid flesh of seal or whale. At one time torches were also used to attract this shark to the surface where it was harpooned and hauled on board.

The principal fishing grounds are the Denmark Straits, western Iceland, Bear Island, Barents Sea, north-western Norway and the Faeroes. As these sharks move around in shoals within their range, each locality within this region has its own local fishing season. During recent years the catches from off the coasts of Greenland, Iceland and Norway have not been of great economic value.

Nowadays Greenland sharks are caught in the open sea, from the deck of a ship. After capture they are hauled on board and hoisted up by capstan. The belly is then slit open and the liver, which weighs 15–20 kg (even up to 300 kg in large individuals), falls out.

When fresh the flesh is poisonous and if not carefully soaked and dried its consumption may cause giddiness, visual disturbance and diarrhoea, in severe cases even paralysis and death. This has frequently been observed in Greenland husky dogs which have been fed on fresh shark meat.

After drying the meat is harmless, but it does not keep well and has a poor flavour, so the remains of the shark are usually thrown overboard after the skin and liver have been removed.

Greenland exports 7,000–8,000 skins annually. The skin can be made into hard wearing leather which is used for bookbinding.

The Greenland shark is, however, primarily caught for its liver, which yields a valuable oil that is particularly rich in vitamin A and is therefore used in vitamin preparations; it was formerly used as a lamp fuel.

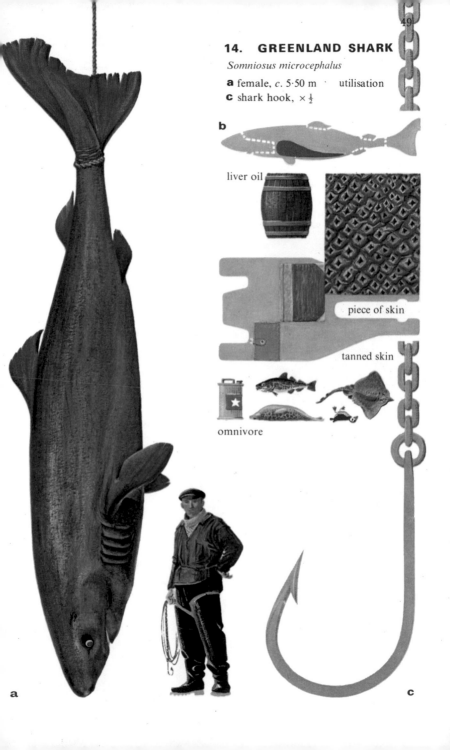

14. GREENLAND SHARK

Somniosus microcephalus

a female, *c.* 5·50 m · utilisation
c shark hook, × ½

b

liver oil

piece of skin

tanned skin

omnivore

a

c

15. Monkfish

Squatina squatina (L.)

A shark with a somewhat ray-like appearance, with large pectoral fins. Average length 90–120 cm, maximum 2·5 m (80 kg). It spends the winter in deep water, but moves in summer to shallow, coastal waters where the female produces 10–25 young, each *c*. 20 cm long.

Monkfish feed mainly on small bottom-living fishes, molluscs and crustaceans. They are of no economic importance. There are in all 14 species in tropical and temperate seas, of which the European form is the largest.

RAYS

Hypotremata

In these fish the head, body and much enlarged pectoral fins are fused to form a disc. The caudal peduncle is long and thin, usually with two small dorsal fins near the rear end. The mouth and the gill openings are on the ventral side, and the eyes on the dorsal side with the spiracles just behind them. The rays are bottom-living fishes, that feed on fish, crustaceans and molluscs which they crush with their flat teeth (see p. 54). Most rays lay eggs, each enclosed in a characteristic large horny capsule (mermaid's purse).

The rays are not easy to identify. They can mostly be distinguished by the shape of the snout and its length measured from the front edge of the eyes. The arrangement of the large dermal spines or thorns can also be used in identification, but this varies somewhat according to age.

16. Marbled Electric ray

Torpedo marmorata Risso

Recognised by the marbled upper surface. The closely related *T. nobiliana*, which occurs to the south of England, is a uniform red-brown, dark green or blue-black on the dorsal side.

The body of an electric ray is almost circular with a short tail and smooth, thornless skin. Maximum length *c*. 1·5 m. These are viviparous fish which feed mainly on small fishes, molluscs and crustaceans. They often occur in shallow water. Not common to the north of the Bay of Biscay and extremely rare in the North Sea.

On each side of its head lies the electric organ, visible through the skin. This consists of modified muscle and nerve tissue, forming a number of vertical hexagonal tubes, each made up of numerous cells. When touched the ray emits a series of short pulses (45–220 volts). The discharge weakens the 'battery' which takes some time to recharge.

Electric ray flesh is not used.

Torpedo nobiliana

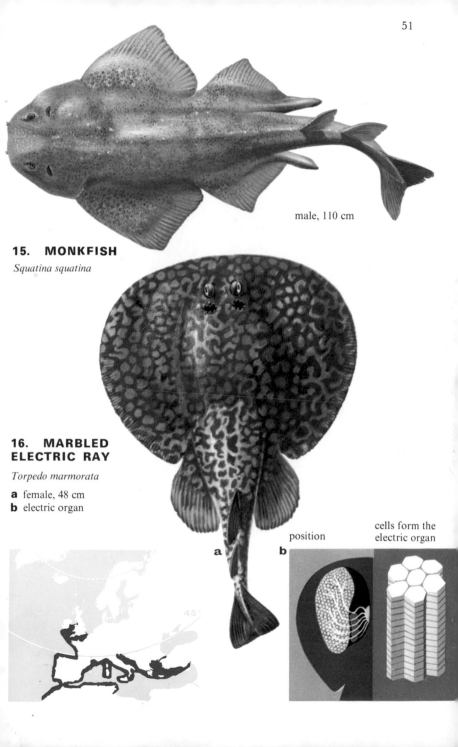

male, 110 cm

15. MONKFISH

Squatina squatina

16. MARBLED ELECTRIC RAY

Torpedo marmorata

a female, 48 cm
b electric organ

position

cells form the
electric organ

a   **b**

17. Thornback ray

Raja clavata L.

Distinctive features: Snout with an obtuse angle, upperside of body with numerous large thorns. The basal plates of these thorns are smooth and shaped like the head of a nail. Also known as the Roker.

Maximum lengths: male 70 cm, female 120 cm. Thornback rays live at depths of 20–100 m, particularly over muddy bottoms. During the course of the summer the female lays about 20 eggs. The rectangular, flattened egg capsules measure 6 × 4 cm. The corners of each capsule

are drawn out into short hollow points. The embryo receives fresh water for respiration through small slits in the capsule wall. The eggs take *c.* 4–5 months to develop. The males become sexually mature at a length of 60 cm and they can be easily distinguished by the rod-like claspers.

Thornback rays feed on crabs, prawns, small flatfishes, sand-eels, etc. They often form part of the trawl catch and can also be taken on a long line, particularly in the North Sea and in British waters. The flesh and liver are used.

18. Starry ray

Raja radiata Donovan

Distinctive features: Snout obtuse, upperside with large thorns whose basal plates are ribbed. Widely distributed in the coastal waters of the North Atlantic.

Average length 60 cm, maximum 100 cm. Lives on muddy and sandy bottoms at depths of 30–200 m, preferring temperatures below 10°C. The egg cases are smaller than those of the thornback ray, and their number and period of incubation are unknown. When hatched the young are 9–10 cm long, and they may become sexually mature at *c.* 40 cm. The males can be distinguished by their claspers. Diet: small fishes (cod, capelin), crabs and prawns. Frequently caught in seines, trawls and on long lines, but of no economic importance.

19. Fylla's ray

Raja fyllae Lütken

Distinctive features: Snout obtuse, pectoral fins equally rounded, the front edge of the disc concave in adults. Irregular longitudinal rows of thorns on back and tail. Underside almost smooth.

Seldom over 55 cm. Lives at depths of 400–1,000 m, in bottom temperatures of 3–6°C. Egg capsules 4 × 2·5 cm, excluding the horns. The young are 7 cm long on hatching. Diet: small bottom-living fishes, crustaceans. Of no economic importance.

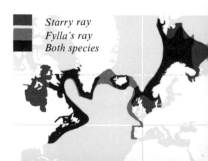

Starry ray
Fylla's ray
Both species

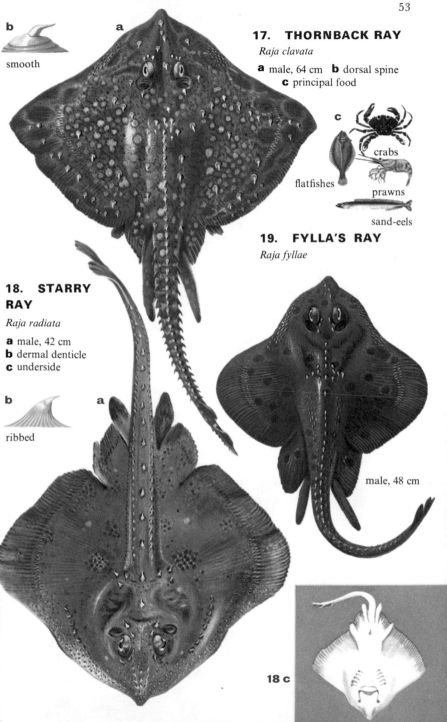

b smooth

a

17. THORNBACK RAY

Raja clavata

a male, 64 cm **b** dorsal spine
c principal food

c

crabs

flatfishes

prawns

sand-eels

19. FYLLA'S RAY

Raja fyllae

18. STARRY RAY

Raja radiata

a male, 42 cm
b dermal denticle
c underside

b ribbed

a

male, 48 cm

18 c

20. Skate

Raja batis L.

Distinctive features: Snout with an acute point, its length 2·5–3·5 times the distance between the eyes. Front edges of the body slightly concave. The small dorsal fins near the tip of the tail almost touch one another. Young specimens with large thorns near the eyes and only one longitudinal row on the back of the tail, older specimens without thorns near the eyes, but with two longitudinal rows, one on each side of the back of the tail. Occasional specimens have all three rows of spines on the tail.

The underside is dark grey, with black spots or stripes, sometimes also with black marbling. Upperside greenish-brown, with or without whitish spots.

The largest Atlantic ray. Average length 1–1·5 m, maximum *c.* 2·5 m, weight up to 100 kg.

Adults live in depths of 100–500 m, but young specimens prefer shallower water.

The eggs are laid in late autumn and winter, and the capsules are at first green, but later become dark brown. They are extraordinarily large (13 × 24 cm) in comparison with those of other rays. The young hatch in 2–5 months, depending upon the

temperature. The males become sexually mature at a length of 1·5 m. Skates are predatory, feeding mainly on various bottom-living fishes, crustaceans and worms.

They are caught on long lines, particularly in late autumn and winter, and also in otter trawls. This is economically the most important ray in north-west Europe. Principal fishing grounds: North Sea, Norwegian coast, Faeroes, south-west Iceland.

The flesh is marketed fresh or smoked. Only the 'wings' (see fig. 20d) and sometimes part of the tail are used.

The liver yields an oil, and small skates are processed into fish meal.

Jaw of female, seen from within. × ½

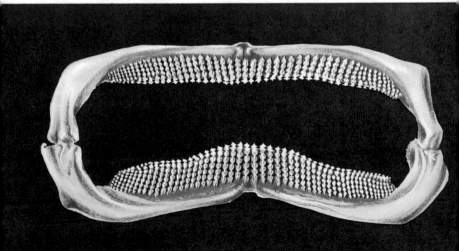

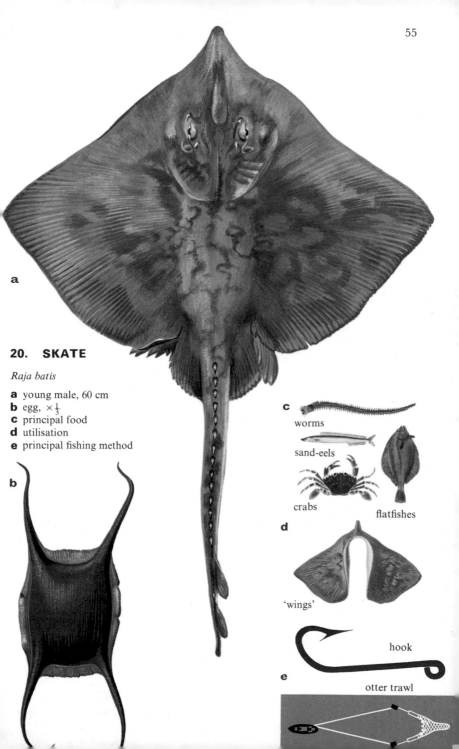

55

20. SKATE

Raja batis

a young male, 60 cm
b egg, $\times \frac{1}{3}$
c principal food
d utilisation
e principal fishing method

c
worms
sand-eels
crabs
flatfishes

d
'wings'

e
hook
otter trawl

56

21. Shagreen ray

Raja fullonica L.

Distinctive features: Snout with an acute point, 3 times as long as the distance between the eyes. Two longitudinal rows of thorns along back of tail. Underside pure white.

Maximum length 1·2 m. Lives in depths of 100–400 m. Probably breeds in deep water. Diet: rabbitfish, velvet belly, cod, crustaceans, molluscs.

Caught on long lines and marketed with skate.

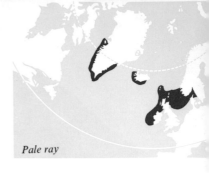

Pale ray

Caught occasionally on long lines but of little value to the fisheries.

23. Long-nosed skate

Raja oxyrinchus L.

Distinctive features: Snout long and pointed, its length 5–6 times the distance between the eyes. Large spines only on the back of the tail. Underside whitish, with small black spots.

Maximum length *c.* 1·5 m. Lives in depths of 100–300 m, and feeds on the velvet belly, redfish, prawns etc. Sexually mature at a length of *c.* 1·2 m. Egg capsules measure *c.* 12 × 6 cm, excluding the horns. Of no economic importance.

22. Pale ray

Raja lintea Fries

Distinctive features: Snout with an acute point, 3½ times as long as the distance

Shagreen ray

between the eyes. One median longitudinal row of large thorns along the back and tail, and two lateral rows on the tail. Underside pure white. Rarely over 1 m, maximum length *c.* 2 m. Lives in depths of 150–200 m. Sexually mature at a length of 1 m. The egg capsules measure 11 × 8 cm, excluding the horns. Feeds mainly on bottom-living fishes, cephalopods, crustaceans.

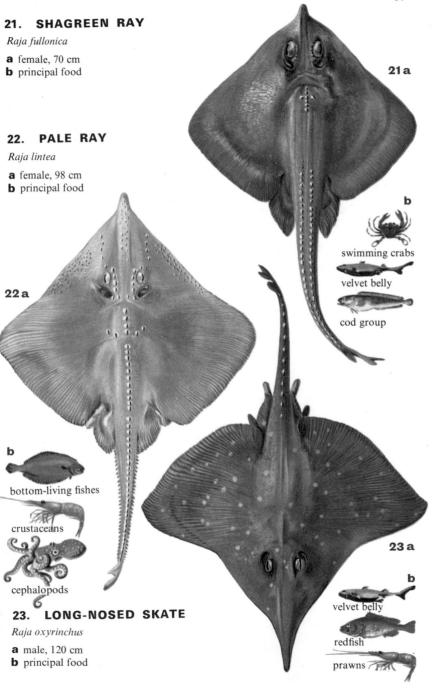

21. SHAGREEN RAY
Raja fullonica

a female, 70 cm
b principal food

21a

22. PALE RAY
Raja lintea

a female, 98 cm
b principal food

22a

b

swimming crabs

velvet belly

cod group

b

bottom-living fishes

crustaceans

cephalopods

23. LONG-NOSED SKATE
Raja oxyrinchus

a male, 120 cm
b principal food

23a

b

velvet belly

redfish

prawns

58

24. Sting ray

Dasyatis pastinaca (L.)

Distinctive features: Tail long and thin without dorsal fins, but with a long, barbed poison spine about half way along its dorsal side.

Average length 0·5–1 m, maximum 2·5 m (*c.* 20 kg). Mainly in shallow waters and often lying buried in the sand during the day. Feeds on small bottom-living fishes, crustaceans, molluscs. The tail spine (8–35 cm long) is shed from time to time and replaced by a new one, and occasional specimens have two spines, one close behind the other. When used in defence the spines can cause very painful wounds; they have a poison gland on the dorsal side.

Sting rays are viviparous and the young are quite large at birth. Several well-known relatives in tropical waters. Of no economic value.

The eagle ray, *Myliobatis aquila,* is a pelagic relative of the sting ray. It has a whip-like tail, a poison spine, large wing-like pectoral fins and a distinct head with lateral eyes. Rare north of the Bay of Biscay.

RABBITFISHES

The Chimaeras or rabbitfishes form a separate group within the cartilaginous fishes. Like the sharks and rays they have a cartilaginous skeleton, but their four gill slits are covered by an operculum (gill cover). There are species in all oceans. They are seldom landed and are not valued on the market.

25. Rabbitfish

Chimaera monstrosa L.

Skin naked. Lateral line distinct, with conspicuous branches on the head. A long, barbed poison spine on the front edge of the dorsal fin.

Maximum length 1·2 m (2·5 kg). The long caudal filament is usually broken in captured specimens. Lives close to the bottom in depths of 200–500 m, but in shallower water during the winter. The flask-shaped eggs measure 17 × 3 cm, and the newly hatched young (11 cm long) resemble the adults. The females are larger than the males and are more frequently caught. The males have a movable, club-shaped outgrowth on the head, which probably serves to anchor the female when mating. Feeds on crustaceans, molluscs, echinoderms and small bottom-living fishes.

Of no economic value, except for the liver which accounts for one-third of the total weight and yields a valuable oil.

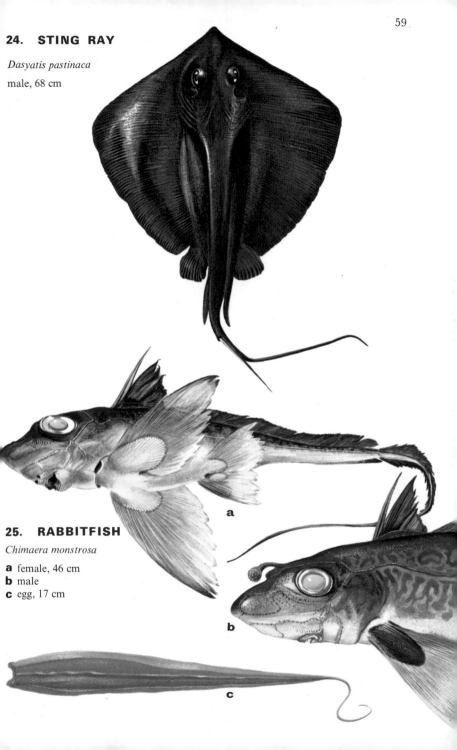

24. STING RAY

Dasyatis pastinaca
male, 68 cm

25. RABBITFISH

Chimaera monstrosa

a female, 46 cm
b male
c egg, 17 cm

a

b

c

BONY FISHES

Osteichthyes

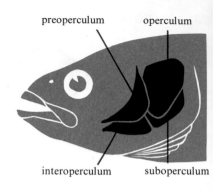

preoperculum   operculum

interoperculum   suboperculum

This group of fishes includes the sturgeons, the tropical lungfishes, a few small orders with primitive structure and the teleosts or true bony fishes with about 19,000 species — by far the majority of the living fishes.

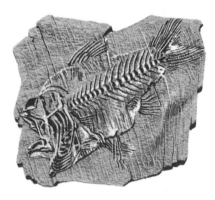

The true bony fishes have evolved during the course of the last 120–150 million years from certain primitive fish groups which are known as fossils from as far back as the Silurian period, about 400 million years ago (see p. 30).

In contrast to the sharks and rays, the bony fishes have an operculum or gill cover over the gill slits, so there is only one aperture between the gills and the outside

world. In some species the external gill opening is reduced to a short slit or small hole (pipefishes, eels). The gill cover is supported by a number of thin bony plates (preoperculum, interoperculum, suboperculum and operculum). The head is also covered by flat dermal bones.

In bony fishes the skeleton is almost completely ossified. The fins are supported by fin rays, which are either articulated and branched or unbranched (soft rays) or unjointed and stiff (spiny or hard rays). In contrast to the sharks and rays, the bony fishes can fold their thin-skinned fins and lay them down on to the body. This mobility of the fin rays is due to the fact that they are loosely linked with the ossified interneural spines, which help to support the dorsal and anal fins. These spines are anchored deep in the body musculature and lie close to the spiny processes of the vertebral column. On the other hand, the rays of the caudal fin are directly supported by the processes of the last caudal vertebra without any intermediate supporting bones.

As a rule the body of a bony fish is covered more or less completely by scales. In several species of the tunny group, for example, only the breast region has an armour of large scales, while the rest of the body and the tail are naked. In other fish species, on the other hand, the skin is furnished with large bony thorns (lump-sucker) or is armoured with bony shields (pipefishes, sticklebacks).

Teeth may be present on all the bones of the mouth and pharynx, and not only on the jaws as is the case in sharks and rays. Pipefishes and some other fishes are toothless.

Many fishes have a swimbladder which arises, during embryonic development, as an evagination from the intestinal tract. In some fish families (herring, salmon, carp, eel) the connection between the oesophagus and the swimbladder remains in the form of an air duct, while in others (cod) this connection is closed. Many bottom-living fishes have no swimbladder (flatfishes, many cottids). The hydrostatic functions of the swimbladder have been discussed in the Introduction (p. 7). It is interesting that a number of open sea fishes, such as mackerel, also lack a swimbladder. These species can, therefore, dive or rise to the surface rapidly, without having to wait for the pressure in the swimbladder to reach equilibrium.

The inner ear of a bony fish is somewhat more complicated than that of the sharks and rays, but it is still a relatively simple structure compared with the auditory organ of birds and mammals. Its upper part consists of three semicircular canals, filled with endolymph, with three ampullae, which enable the fish to orientate itself in space. The lower part has three chambers each of which contains an otolith. The otoliths consist mainly of calcium. As the fish grows, the otoliths, like the scales, lay down growth rings which can be used in age determination (see p. 235). The two lower otoliths react to sound waves, while the upper one helps to maintain equilibrium.

Most bony fishes release eggs and sperm directly into the water. In viviparous fishes there is a form of copulation and internal fertilisation (e.g. livebearing toothcarps). Pelagic eggs are small, but are produced in large numbers, since the wastage rate is high. Demersal eggs, i.e. those that sink to the bottom after spawning or adhere to

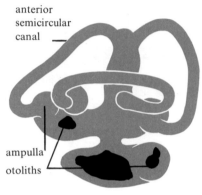

anterior semicircular canal ___

ampulla
otoliths

auditory organ

rocks and plants, are usually larger and fewer in numbers. Many fishes that live among coastal seaweeds practise a simple form of brood care which serves to protect the eggs and young during their early stages. The larvae of most bony fishes have to pass through a more or less critical stage, known as metamorphosis, before they begin to look like the adults.

During the course of their evolution the bony fishes have invaded every type of water on the earth's surface, from high mountain lakes to subterranean waters and the greatest depths in the sea.

One of the largest bony fishes is the tunny which reaches a length of c. 3 m and a weight of 300 kg. One of the smallest is a goby in the Philippines which is only 12 mm long and weighs 0·065 gram.

Several of the bony fishes are of economic importance and are subject to planned commercial fishing, others are only caught incidentally. The annual landings throughout the world amount to approximately 60 million tons, of which Europe accounts for c. 23 million tons. Over 50 per cent of the European catch consists of the following 10 species: cod, haddock, whiting, saithe (coalfish), pilchard, anchovy, mackerel, plaice, herring and hake.

STURGEONS

The sturgeons show a number of primitive characters and are therefore classified in their own group within the bony fishes. There are about 26 different species, most of which occur in Russian or Asiatic waters where they are of great importance to the fisheries. In the Soviet Union the annual catch in the Black Sea and Caspian Sea areas is about 12,000 to 16,000 tons.

26. Sturgeon

Acipenser sturio L.

Body shark-like with five longitudinal rows of bony plates. The head is armoured with dermal bones. The fins are supported by cartilaginous rays, and the caudal fin has an enlarged upper lobe (heterocercal tail). The first rays of the pectoral fins are fused to form a powerful spine. The small, toothless mouth can be protruded like a trunk, and in front of it there are 4 barbels arranged in a horizontal row.

Average length 1–2 m, maximum 5–6 m (400 kg, longevity over 100 years). Individuals with a length of 2–3 m are very rarely caught nowadays.

Sturgeons spend the greater part of their life in the sea. The males are sexually mature at an age of 7–9 years and a length of 110–150 cm, the females at 8–14 years and 120–180 cm. In the period April-June they move up into the rivers of Europe where they spawn. Some migrate far upstream, e.g. in the Rhine up to Speyer, others remain close to the sea. They spawn in depths of 2–10 m over stony bottoms, the female producing 800,000–2,400,000 sticky, dark grey eggs which adhere to the stones. After spawning the adults move back into the sea. The eggs, which are c. 3 mm in diameter, hatch after 3–6 days into larvae that are about 9 mm long. After a period of 1–2 years at the most, the young fish migrate to the sea where they remain until they are sexually mature.

Sturgeons feed mainly on insect larvae, molluscs and worms which they dig out of soft bottoms with the long snout and suck up with the tubular mouth. Older individuals also take fish.

Owing to pollution of the rivers and overfishing during the spawning period sturgeons are now very rare in western and central Europe. They are occasionally caught in trawls, seine nets and drift nets.

The roe of the ripe females is used in the production of caviar. The ovaries are carefully cut open, and the eggs sieved to remove mucus. They are then rubbed with salt or put in brine and slightly compressed, before being packed in casks or boxes made of oak or lime wood. The best caviar comes from the Hausen, a large species from southern Russia. The flesh is also very tasty; in Russia the dorsal region is smoked and dried to give 'balyk'. The swimbladder yields isinglass.

Sturgeon are of very little economic importance in western Europe.

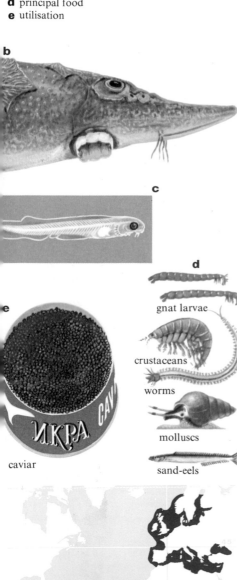

26. **STURGEON**

Acipenser sturio

a 105 cm
b head with mouth protruded
c larva
d principal food
e utilisation

b

c

d

gnat larvae

crustaceans

worms

molluscs

sand-eels

e

ИКРА CAV

caviar

HERRING-LIKE FISHES

The herring and related species are slender, pelagic fishes with a short dorsal fin and no lateral line. They live in shoals, which often reach enormous sizes. They feed principally on planktonic animals which they sieve from the water entering the mouth by their gill filtration apparatus; sometimes they also snap up larger planktonic animals. These fishes are themselves eaten by mackerel and haddock.

The muscle tissue of the members of the herring family has a high content of fat, and so they are particularly suitable for smoking; they also have very soft bones. The family in fact supplies a third, or 20 million tons, of the total world production of fish. The yield of the different countries fluctuates because the shoals may suddenly change their migration routes. About 11 million tons are used in the production of oil and fish meal.

Key

1 {
Upper jaw protruding .... **Anchovy,** p. 70

Lower jaw protruding **2**

2 {
Gill cover smooth **3**

Gill cover with radial stripes; 1–6 black spots on each flank **4**

3 {
Base of ventral fins behind front end of dorsal fin .... **Herring,** p. 65

Base of ventrals in front or beneath front end of dorsal fin .... **Sprat,** p. 69

4 {
About 30 large scales along middle of each flank .... **Pilchard,** p. 70

60–80 scales along middle of each flank .... **Allis shad,** p. 72
Twaite shad, p. 72

27. Herring

Clupea harengus L.

The base of the ventral fins lies behind the front end of the dorsal fin. The keel scales are not so sharp as in the sprat. Gill cover smooth, without radial stripes.

Herring seldom reach a length of more than 40 cm, or an age of more than 20–25 years. They are pelagic (free-swimming) and live at depths down to 250 m. They occur particularly in those regions of the north Atlantic where the warm water masses coming from the south (Gulf Stream) mix with the cold, arctic currents. Their shoals reach enormous proportions, sometimes containing several thousand tons of fish. They spend the day in deeper water, but rise to the surface at night.

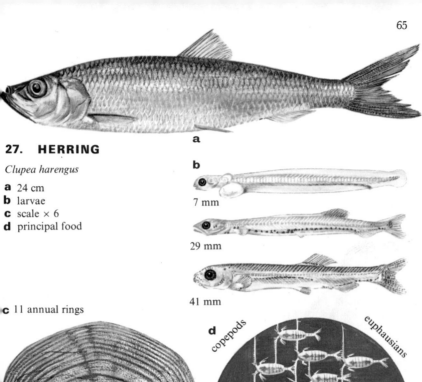

27.   HERRING

Clupea harengus

a 24 cm
b larvae
c scale × 6
d principal food

7 mm

29 mm

41 mm

c 11 annual rings

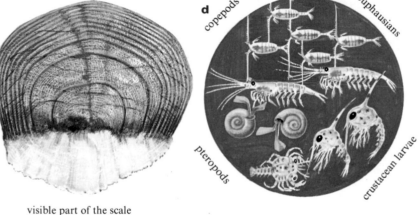

copepods

euphausians

pteropods

crustacean larvae

visible part of the scale

The herring can be divided into different races, which are mainly distinguished by size, rate of growth, spawning period and migration routes, and also by the number of vertebrae, the otoliths and the scales, from which an experienced biologist can tell the growth history and the spawning periods. The most important herring races in the east Atlantic are the White Sea herring, the Murman herring, the winter-spawning Norwegian herring and the Baltic herring. In addition, there are numerous local races of coastal herring. The Norwegian herring is the most important from the fisheries viewpoint and so its life cycle is briefly described here.

During the winter months the large herring move from the North Sea to the west coast of Norway. Immediately after their arrival they become sexually mature; their sexual products which are still firm during the migration to the coast now become ripe and fluid. Spawning takes place along the Norwegian coast in February-April, mainly in the transition zone between the coastal water and the warmer, more saline deep water, and particularly at depths of 40–70 m and temperatures around 5°C. A single female produces 20,000–50,000 eggs, and these are shed freely into the water, as are the sperms of the males. The fertilised eggs (1·2–1·5 mm diameter) sink to the bottom where they adhere to rocks, algae and mollusc shells. It has been estimated that 1–3 million tons of eggs are spawned annually off the Norwegian coast alone. At a temperature of 9°C the eggs hatch in about 2 weeks. The newly hatched larvae (7–9 mm) are attracted by the light and rise to the surface. After a week they have consumed their reserve of yolk and they now start to feed on microscopic planktonic algae and crustacean larvae. The scales form when they are about 4 cm long. During the course of the first year the brood spreads out along the whole Norwegian coast, and it is only when they are 2–3 years old, and about 20 cm long, that they move away from the coast. The immature individuals, 20–30 cm long, have a large amount of fat deposited in the muscles and between the internal organs. Herring become sexually mature at an age of 3–7 years and from then on they take part in the annual spawning migrations. As soon as they have spawned they move north-west in search of food.

During this migration they are fished off the Faeroes and northern Iceland. They migrate as far as the boundary of the cold East Iceland current in the area between Jan Mayen and Iceland and feed there on the rich plankton. By late autumn they turn back towards the Norwegian coast. The Murman herring spawns off the coasts of the Barents Sea in March-April and move from there into the northern and eastern part of this sea. The individual populations in the North Sea are particularly difficult to distinguish from one another; there are several local races of spring, summer and autumn spawners. By far the most important are the autumn herring, of which there is a northern form, the bank herring, and a southern form, the down herring.

Both forms are found from May to July in the northern North Sea (Fladen Ground) where they grow fat and mature. The bank herring starts to spawn in July off the Scottish North Sea coast. From there it moves across the central North Sea in September-October to the Skagerrak where it spends the winter months. In April it returns to its feeding grounds in the Fladen Ground. The down herring, on the other hand, spawns in late autumn, migrating from the Fladen Ground to the southern North Sea, where it spawns in October-January. It spends the winter in the Straits of Dover and returns to the Fladen Ground in March.

The Baltic herring also has a spring-spawning and an autumn-spawning population. It becomes sexually mature at an age of 2–3 years when 10–12 cm long, and reaches a length of 20 cm at the most. The Russians have succeeded in introducing the Baltic herring into the brackish Aral Sea to the east of the Caspian Sea.

Adult herring feed on animal plankton, particularly on copepods, euphausians and pteropods, and in the North Sea also on sand-eel larvae. They feed by sight and so mainly by day. They also feed less during the winter months, and grow less.

The herring shoals are located with the help of echo-sounding equipment; from the echo trace it is possible to estimate the depth, direction of swimming and size of a shoal. Sometimes one can see a shoal with the naked eye as a violet patch in the water, or its presence may be betrayed by the thousands of attendant sea birds. As herring rise to the surface the water pressure is reduced and they are able rapidly to get rid of some of the gas in the swimbladder through a special air duct

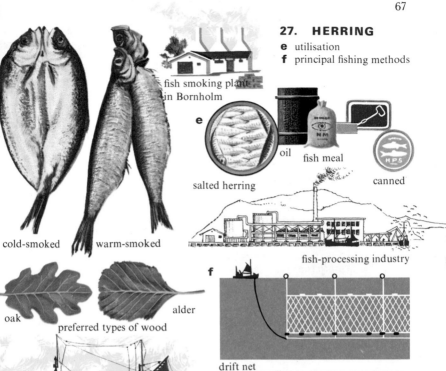

27. HERRING
e utilisation
f principal fishing methods

fish smoking plant in Bornholm

oil

fish meal

canned

salted herring

cold-smoked

warm-smoked

fish-processing industry

oak

alder

preferred types of wood

f

drift net

purse seine

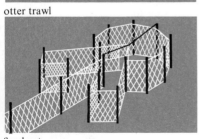

PD.1963   TOVE

British fishing boat

otter trawl

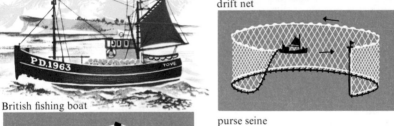

fixed net

which opens to the outside at the anus. When this happens the sea appears to be 'boiling', from the millions of little air bubbles, and this tells the fisherman that a shoal is moving upwards.

Fishing for Norwegian herring is done mainly with drift nets (at night) and with purse seines. Near the coast, spring herring are also caught in fixed nets. In the North Sea, herring are caught by trawl during the day, by drift net at night. Coastal herring are also caught in beach seines.

Young herring, 1–2 years old, are caught and processed into oil and fish meal, and some are also canned. Most larger herring are marketed fresh, salted or canned.

Total catch in the Atlantic and adjacent waters: 2–3 million tons per year. Of this Norway takes 250,000 tons, the Soviet Union 240,000–260,000 tons, Denmark c. 300,000 tons, Sweden 120,000–200,000 tons, Germany 150,000 tons, Great Britain 100,000–150,000 tons, Poland 120,000–140,000 tons, Iceland 50,000–70,000 tons, Holland 50,000 tons, Faeroes 45,000–70,000 tons, Ireland 30,000–40,000 tons, France 25,000 tons.

28. Sprat

Sprattus sprattus (L.)

The base of the ventral fins lies in front of or below the front end of the dorsal fin. The keels of the scales between the ventral fins and the anal fin are sharp, with backward-directed points.

Sexually mature at an age of 2 years when 12–13 cm long; maximum length 16·5 cm, longevity 5–6 years. Pelagic shoaling fishes in fjords and waters near the coast, in summer at depths of 10–50 m, in winter down to 150 m. By day the shoal

remains close to the bottom, but at night the fish rise towards the surface and the shoal more or less breaks up. The species has several races and subspecies within its geographical range.

Spawns in January–July, but mainly in May–June, mostly at depths of 10–20 m, producing 6,000 to 10,000 pelagic eggs. Principal spawning area: south-eastern North Sea and Skagerrak. There are local populations in the large fjords, in the Danish Belt and in the Baltic Sea. The eggs have a diameter of 0·8–1·5 mm, and are largest when in brackish water; they hatch in c. 7 days. The newly hatched larvae are 4 mm long and similar to those of the herring. They are driven far from the spawning area by sea currents: from the Skagerrak, for example, northwards along the coast of western Norway. They reach a length of c. 10 cm when one year old. Sprat feed on animal plankton, particularly copepods. They themselves form an important part of the diet of numerous predatory fishes.

Caught in trawls, seines or beach seines; in the Baltic Sea also in fixed nets. The catch fluctuates considerably, but as it consists primarily of one and two year old fish, a poor spawning season is quickly reflected in the fishery yield. A great number of the eggs die if the weather is cold and windy during the spawning season.

The Soviet Union 100,000–140,000 tons, Great Britain 40,000–50,000 tons, Poland 15,000–30,000 tons, Germany 15,000–25,000 tons, Denmark 5,000–35,000 tons, Norway 8,000–16,000 tons, Sweden 4,000–6,000 tons.

In Norway the one year old sprats have to be kept for 3 days, so that the gut is emptied, before they are preserved smoked, cooked or in oil (brisling). The 2–4 year old sprats are marinated and marketed as 'anchovies'. Similar methods of preservation in Sweden, Denmark and Germany. A proportion of the catch is processed into fish meal.

28. SPRAT

Sprattus sprattus

a 10 cm
b keel scales × 8
c principal food
d utilisation
e principal fishing methods

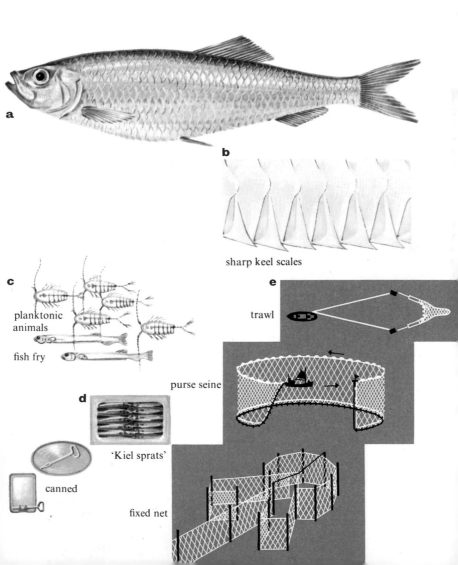

a

b

sharp keel scales

c planktonic animals

fish fry

d 'Kiel sprats'

canned

e trawl

purse seine

fixed net

29. Pilchard or Sardine

Sardina pilchardus (Walbaum)

Distinctive features: Gill cover with radial striations. Ventral fins lying below the rear end of the dorsal fin. Thirty scales along the mid-line on each side.

Sexually mature at an age of 3 years and a length of 19–20 cm. Maximum length *c.* 26 cm (*c.* 15 years). Pelagic shoaling fishes that feed on planktonic crustaceans and fish eggs. Spawns in the open sea, producing 50,000–60,000 pelagic eggs, off southern England in April-November, in the Bay of Biscay in December-February, off Portugal February-April, and throughout the whole year in the Mediterranean. The eggs hatch in 2–4 days into larvae that are 4 mm long.

After spawning, pilchards move to their feeding grounds in the vicinity of the coast, going northwards in summer, southwards in winter. Probably only occurring sporadically in the North Sea.

Caught with drift nets and seines, and frequently lured with lights in the Mediterranean. Salted cod roe, sometimes mixed with sand and pieces of meat, is used as bait.

The annual catch in Europe fluctuates between 450,000 and 550,000 tons, of which 25–35 per cent is salted, canned in oil, and marketed as sardines. Spain lands 110,000–130,000 tons, Portugal 60,000–100,000 tons, Italy and France 30,000–40,000 tons each, Yugoslavia 10,000–15,000 tons, Greece 10,000 tons, Great Britain 1,000 tons.

There are several related species in other parts of the world, and these are also economically valuable.

30. Anchovy

Engraulis encrasicolus (L.)

Distinctive features: Mouth distinctly ventral; body coloration characteristic. Ventral fins lying in front of the dorsal fin.

Seldom over 16 cm long. Sexually mature at 2 years (9–12 cm). There are five geographical races, of which that in the Sea of Azov is only 10 cm, that in the Mediterranean 12·5 cm. Pelagic shoaling fishes which feed on animal plankton. The females produce 13,000–20,000 oval, pelagic eggs which hatch in 2–4 days into larvae that are 3 mm long. Spawning periods: June-August in the southern North Sea, April-September in the Mediterranean, May-August in the Sea of Azov. The eggs are shed in batches over a long period.

In summer, these fish migrate to the vicinity of the coast, and sometimes into brackish water, but in winter they move into deeper water. They are caught in drift nets and seines or in fish traps. The annual catch in Europe fluctuates between 230,000 and 340,000 tons; in addition some 18,000 tons are caught in the Kertch Strait in the Sea of Azov. Anchovies are landed in the following countries: the Soviet Union 80,000–150,000 tons, Italy 40,000–50,000 tons, Turkey 30,000–55,000 tons, Spain 50,000–60,000 tons, Greece 7,000 tons, Portugal 1,000–7,000 tons.

Anchovy flesh has a bitter taste. The head and entrails are often removed. The body is salted and packed in barrels, but they need a period of 4–18 months storage for maturing. A proportion of the catch is filleted and packed in oil. There are several related and economically valuable species in other parts of the world.

29. PILCHARD

Sardina pilchardus

a 18 cm
b principal food
c utilisation
d principal fishing methods

b

fish eggs

copepods

29 c

fresh on ice

**29 c
30 c**

canned

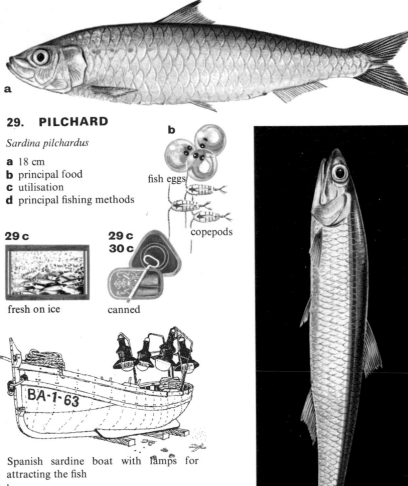

Spanish sardine boat with lamps for attracting the fish

d drift net

purse seine

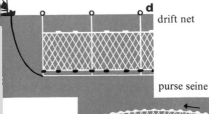

a

30. ANCHOVY

Engraulis encrasicolus

a 16 cm
b principal food
c utilisation
d principal fishing method

SHADS

The fishes in this group, represented by two species in Europe, migrate from the sea into fresh water to spawn. The eggs develop over a period of 2–8 days, while drifting. In autumn the young fish move back into the sea. They are caught in river estuaries while swimming up to spawn; the stocks are now much reduced, partly because of the increasing pollution of European rivers. They feed on plant and animal plankton.

31. Twaite shad

Alosa fallax (Lacépède)

Distinctive features: 60–65 scales in a longitudinal row; 6–10 black spots on each flank. First gill arch with 40–60 gill rakers (fig. 31b). Caught off northern Germany but of no great economic importance; marketed as smoked fish.

32. Allis shad

Alosa alosa (L.)

Distinctive features: 70–80 scales in a longitudinal row; 1–6 more or less distinct spots on each flank. First gill arch with 90–120 gill rakers (fig. 32). Caught in the Bay of Biscay and in the Mediterranean but of no economic importance.

The allis shad is very similar in external appearance to the twaite shad, but can be distinguished by its dense, well-developed gill rakers.

33. Hatchetfish

Argyropelecus olfersi (Cuvier)

With numerous light organs on the head and flanks. Back with a bony ridge in front of the dorsal fin, and a low adipose fin.

Maximum length *c*. 12 cm. An oceanic deep-sea fish which lives in depths of 300 m, where it is fairly abundant.

There are a few closely related species in the north-east Atlantic.

34. Sheppy argentine

Maurolicus muelleri (Gmelin)

Also known as the pearl-side.

With light organs along the underside, and a low adipose fin behind the dorsal fin. Length 7 cm. Oceanic and pelagic in depths of 150 m. Rises towards the surface at night and is then found among small herring and sprats. During the winter months it is often washed ashore along the coasts of the north-east Atlantic.

Twaite shad
Allis shad
Both species

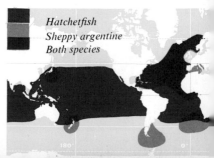

Hatchetfish
Sheppy argentine
Both species

a

b

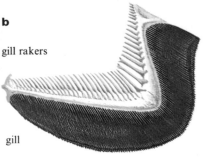

gill rakers

gill rakers

gill

gill

31. TWAITE SHAD

Alosa fallax

a 41 cm
b gill arch, natural size

32. ALLIS SHAD

Alosa alosa

33. HATCHETFISH

Argyropelecus olfersi

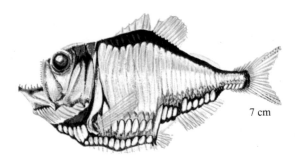

7 cm

34. SHEPPY ARGENTINE

Maurolicus muelleri

6 cm

35. Salmon

Salmo salar L.

The salmon is not easy to distinguish from trout. Its body is more slender and the caudal peduncle is narrower. Between the adipose fin and the lateral line there are (including the lateral line scale) 11–15 scales (most commonly 12–14). The gill rakers of the first gill arch are all slender (p. 79).

Maximum length of male 150 cm (36 kg), female rarely over 120 cm (20 kg). Longevity 4–6, rarely 10 years. Large salmon start to migrate from the sea to the coasts in May, smaller individuals follow somewhat later, and both have large reserves of fat. From this time until after spawning they scarcely feed at all.

The spawning migration into fresh water lasts from June to November. During this period their fat reserves are converted into energy and into the sexual products. At the same time the colours change from silvery blue-green to brownish or greenish with orange or red mottling. In the adult males the lower jaw forms a hook, and there is active fighting between rival individuals. Spawning takes place in late autumn, in cool, clean streams, at depths of 0·5–3 m. The female chooses a suitable site with a sandy or gravelly bottom and digs a spawning nest or redd by lateral flexion of her body and tail region. In this nest she lays a number of yellow, pea-sized eggs which are fertilised by the male and covered with gravel, while the female prepares another pit for the next spawning. The spawning period may extend over a period of more than two weeks, and often several nests are used. The total number of eggs laid is 8,000–26,000. The eggs are heavier than water, slightly sticky and lie embedded among the gravel throughout the winter.

After the considerable efforts expended in migration and in the actual process of spawning the fish are very emaciated. They will have lost 30–40% of their pre-spawning weight. Many die after spawning, particu-

a

35. SALMON

Salmo salar

a adult from the sea, 68 cm
b scale of a 5 year old salmon
c larva (25 mm) with yolk sac
d principal food in the sea

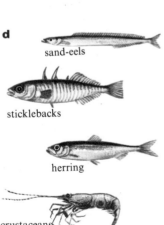

c

b

growth rings in fresh water

1st year
2nd year

the sea
d year
h year
year

spawning mark

d

sand-eels

sticklebacks

herring

crustaceans

visible part of scale

larly males, others spend the winter in deeper parts of the river or return immediately to the sea. Only 4–6% spawn a second time and perhaps one in a thousand a third time. Those that reach the sea recover fairly rapidly.

The eggs hatch into larvae in April–May. The larvae, which are 20 mm long, have a yolk sac which supplies them with nutriment for $1\frac{1}{2}$ months. After this they start to hunt for insect larvae and small worms. Depending upon the spawning locality the young salmon remain 1–5 years in fresh water (the longest period in northern Norway, but only one year in the Rhine). A few of the males may even remain in fresh water until they are sexually mature, but most migrate to the sea at a length of 10–19 cm. During the descent their coloration changes: the grey-blue spots on the sides disappear, the back becomes dark and the flanks silvery.

They spend some time in the estuaries while they acclimatise to the salinity of sea water and to the change in diet. They now feed mainly on copepods and other crustaceans, and later on small fish.

The young salmon grow only slowly in fresh water, but very rapidly in the sea. Their lengths and weights are: after 1 year 50–65 cm and 1·5–3·5 kg, after 2 years 70–90 cm and 4–8 kg, after 3 years 90–105 cm and 8–13 kg. In the sea they lead a pelagic and predatory life near the surface, feeding on small fish and crustaceans. After spending 2–3 years in the sea they migrate back to their native waters where they spawn. An astonishing instinct takes them back to the waters in which they grew up. It is thought that they are led there by the sense of smell. Marking experiments have shown that their migrations cover distances of several thousand kilometres, with average speeds of 50–100 km per day.

There are land-locked races of salmon, that are often dwarfed, in certain large lakes that are no longer connected with the sea.

The life history of a salmon can be read from the growth zones in the scales: the 'lean' years in fresh water, the rapid growth in the sea, as well as the age and the spawning periods.

The capture of salmon in fresh waters is outside the scope of this book. In the sea they are mainly fished during their migrations along the coast. They are caught in drift nets, fixed traps and also with floating long lines, several kilometres long, baited with herring.

Salmon are caught by fishermen from the following countries: Norway, Denmark, Sweden, Britain, Germany, Iceland, Poland, the Soviet Union and Canada.

They are marketed fresh, smoked and canned.

All the countries that fish for salmon have introduced well-defined closed seasons, but the greatest enemies of this fish are regulations involving damming and the control of water flow, and also the ever-increasing pollution of rivers.

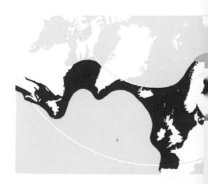

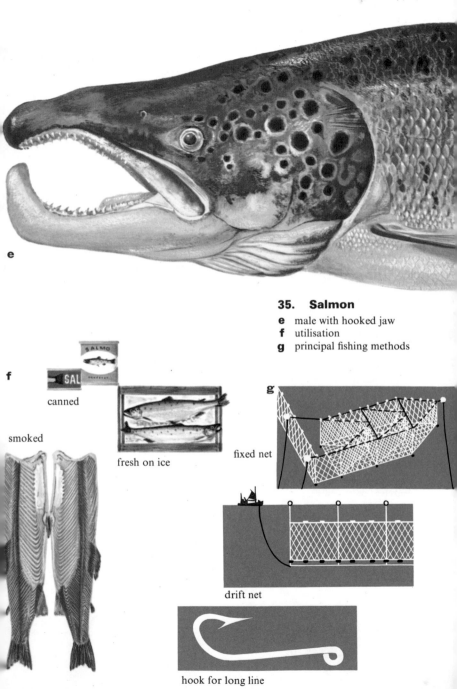

35. Salmon

e male with hooked jaw
f utilisation
g principal fishing methods

f

canned

smoked

fresh on ice

g

fixed net

drift net

hook for long line

36. TROUT

Salmo trutta L.

Distinguished from salmon by the plumper body and the taller caudal peduncle. There are 14–19 (usually 16) scales between the adipose fin and the lateral line (including the lateral line scale). On the first gill arch the first 2–5 upper and lower gill rakers are blunt, whereas the central rakers are slender (fig. 36 b).

Rarely over 80–100 cm and 10–15 kg. Longevity 4–6 years.

Life history very similar to that of the salmon, but does not undertake such extensive migrations in the sea, and has freshwater forms which do not enter the sea: river trout spend their whole life in the upland reaches of rivers, whereas lake trout spawn in rivers but grow up in the lakes. Sea trout are those forms that spend part of their life in the sea; their migrations, spawning habits and development are similar to those of salmon. During their stay in fresh water they feed on aquatic insects and—to a greater extent than salmon—on flying insects. When 15–25 cm long they migrate to the sea where they stay in the vicinity of the coast for $\frac{1}{2}$–5 years, feeding on crustaceans and small fishes. After one year in the sea they are 30–40 cm (0·4 kg), after 2 years 40–50 cm (1–1·5 kg), after 3 years 50–60 cm (1·5–3·5 kg). When they move up into the rivers for spawning in July-November they acquire an attractive breeding coloration. The female lays up to about 10,000 eggs. Most of the adults survive and spawn again the following year.

Sea trout are popular sporting fish, being caught on artificial flies and on spinners. They are taken commercially in drift nets.

37. Rainbow Trout

Salmo gairdneri Richardson

Distinguished by the broad, reddish iridescent band along each flank.

Introduced into Europe from California about 1890. They are less sensitive to the temperature and composition of the water than trout and salmon. As their growth is very rapid they are in many places raised in artificial ponds on trout farms. In open waters they may migrate into the sea where they are occasionally caught. They spawn in early spring. Maximum length *c.* 70 cm (7 kg).

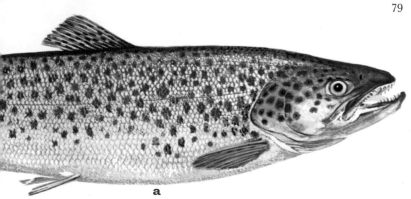

a

36. TROUT

Salmo trutta

a male, 47 cm, September
b first gill arch
c principal food in the sea

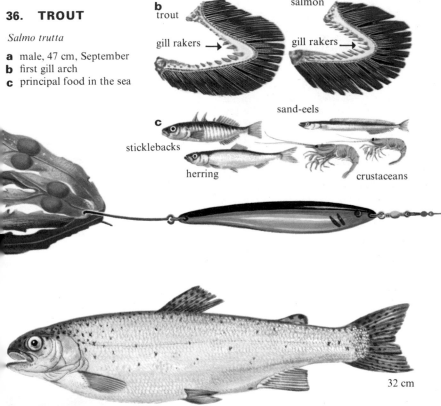

b
trout

salmon

gill rakers

gill rakers

c

sand-eels

sticklebacks

herring

crustaceans

32 cm

37. RAINBOW TROUT

Salmo gairdneri

38. Lesser argentine

Argentina sphyraena L.

Characteristics: Snout longer than or as long as the diameter of the eye. 52–53 lateral line scales. With a smell like cucumber.

Maximum length 27 cm. Lives close to the bottom or pelagically in depths of 30–100 m. The eggs and young are pelagic. Feed on crustaceans and worms. The scales from this fish, together with those from herring and pilchard, are used in the preparation of pearl essence (essence d'Orient) for artificial pearls and nail varnish.

39. Larger argentine

Argentina silus Ascanius

Characteristics: Snout shorter than the eye diameter. 66–70 lateral line scales. Smells of cucumber. Maximum length 50 cm. Lives as a pelagic, shoaling fish in depths of 150–1,000 m. The eggs and young are pelagic, in deep water. Feed on fishes, euphausians and other pelagic crustaceans.

Caught on hooks and in prawn nets, and used for fish meal.

40. Smelt

Osmerus eperlanus (L.)

Salmon-like fish with at the most 80 scales in a longitudinal row. Smells of cucumber.

In the sea smelts become sexually mature at an age of 3–4 years and a length of 15–18 cm; they are rarely longer than 20 cm (*c.* 6 years). A subspecies from northern Siberia grows longer. The main European form lives as a pelagic, shoaling and migratory fish which enters the lower reaches of rivers in April-May where it spawns. The female produces 9,000–40,000 eggs (diameter 0·6–0·9 mm) which adhere to water plants and sand grains. These hatch in 3–5 weeks. There are isolated forms in the deep inland lakes of the Baltic region, which were probably left from the time when the sea covered large areas of Scandinavia after the last Ice Age.

Diet: insect larvae, small crustaceans.

Used for feeding cattle, for the preparation of oil and to a small extent as human food.

41. Capelin

Mallotus villosus (Müller)

A salmon-like fish with at least 150 scales in a longitudinal row. Adult males have shaggy outgrowths on the large lateral line scales.

Capelin become sexually mature at 2–4 years and a length of 15–20 cm (males) and 13–17 cm (females); the Pacific sub-species grows larger. They live as pelagic shoaling fishes, by day at depths of 150 m, by night close to surface. In December they form large shoals which move from the Barents Sea to Murmansk and Finnmark. They spawn at a temperature of 2–4°C. Mating takes 5 seconds and the 8,000–12,000 adhesive eggs (diameter 0·6–1·2 mm) are laid in a sand furrow at depths of 5–100 m. The males die after spawning. Some of the females survive and spawn again in the following 2–3 years. The eggs hatch in *c.* 4 weeks into larvae that are 4–5 mm long. Capelin feed on animal plankton.

They form an important part of the diet of cod and saithe and of whales. They are caught in seine nets off Finnmark, and are processed in fish factories.

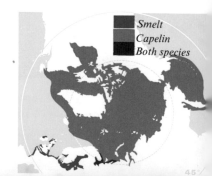

Smelt
Capelin
Both species

18 cm

38. LESSER ARGENTINE
Argentina sphyreana

48 cm

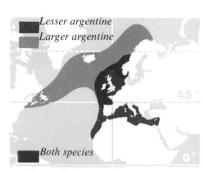

Lesser argentine
Larger argentine

45°

Both species

0°

39. LARGER ARGENTINE
Argentina silus

40. SMELT
Osmerus eperlanus

7 cm

a

b

41. CAPELIN
Mallotus villosus

a male, 16 cm
b female, 14 cm
c utilisation
d principal fishing method

c

fish processing

d seine net

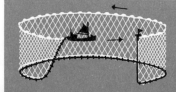

42.   Common Eel

Anguilla anguilla (L.)

The peculiar life history of the European eel starts in the Sargasso Sea area, about 4,000 km from Europe. Here the smallest known eel larvae, about 5 mm in length, are found in March-April in depths of 100–300 m in an area where the sea floor lies at a depth of about 6,000 m. The body of this *leptocephalus* larva is transparent and band-like. These larvae live a pelagic life in the upper waters of the sea and are carr by the Gulf Stream across the Atlantic Europe. Their journey lasts almost th years. Shortly before they arrive at coasts of Europe they metamorphose i still colourless elvers, which are about mm long and slightly shorter than *leptocephalus*. The elvers move i brackish water areas and start to move

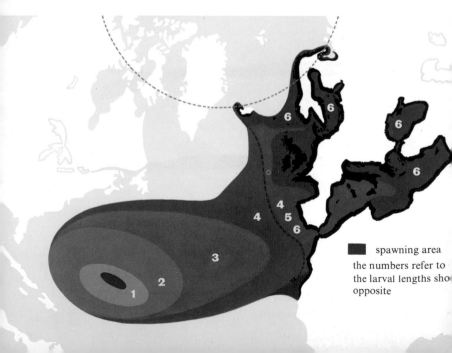

spawning area

the numbers refer to the larval lengths sho opposite

42. COMMON EEL

Anguilla anguilla

a yellow eel, 40 cm
b silver eel, 38 cm
c yellow eel, from above
d silver eel, from above
e growth and metamorphosis of the larva
f map showing larval distribution

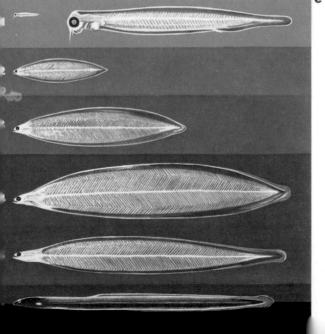

e

7 mm
just hatched
× 10

25 mm
c. 2 months

45 mm
c. 8 months

75 mm
c. 1½ years

70 mm
c. 2½ years

65 mm
c. 3 years old

the rivers (in Spain and Ireland in November-December, on the North Sea coasts and in the Kattegat in March-April). They are particularly numerous in the Bristol Channel.

During the course of the summer, after feeding well, the elvers become darkly pigmented. Some of them remain in the brackish water of the estuaries and in the lower reaches of the rivers, but the others move upstream and spend the following years in fresh water. When about 3 years

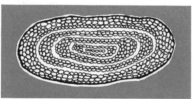

scale with growth zones

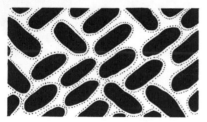

scale pattern

old they start to develop the tiny oval scales which lie embedded in the skin.

The growth of the young eels depends upon the food supply and the water temperature. In the first winter after their arrival at the coast they are c. 8 cm long, in the second winter 17–19 cm. During this period of feeding and growth they are known as yellow eels: the eyes are small, the snout broad, the back is grey-brown and the sides and belly yellowish.

Eels are crepuscular and they feed on worms, molluscs, copepods, insect larvae, shrimps, crabs, sticklebacks and gobies.

Those which feed mainly on largish anim have a fairly broad snout, whereas tho that take small invertebrates have pointed snout. However, both typ belong to the same species and there a many intermediate forms. During the co part of the year the eels move into deep frost-free places, and spend the wint buried in the mud.

At an age of 6–7 years many eels beg to undergo a remarkable series of change Their eyes become enlarged, the he becomes pointed, the skin on the ba darker, while that on the belly becom shiny and silvery. Gradually they st feeding, the alimentary canal regresses, b the body becomes firm and muscular: t yellow eels have changed into silver ee It has been thought that the eels th remained in brackish water become mal those from rivers and lakes females, b this is not always the case. The mal change earlier into silver eels, the femal not until they are about 8–10 years ol Male silver eels are 29–51 cm long, femal 42–100 cm. Maximum weight c. 3·5 k The sex organs are still small and u developed. By suitable hormone treatme it is possible to induce the males to becom sexually mature (fig. 42h).

In September-October the silver ee migrate into the sea and disappear into t depths of the Atlantic Ocean. It is thoug that the sex organs ripen in the Sargass Sea; sexually mature males have only be found on three occasions off the coasts Europe.

How the eels reach the Sargasso Sea still a matter of some uncertainty. The have never been observed outside t European coastal region, apart from single specimen found in the stomach of sperm whale. Even in the North Sea, ee are very rarely caught. One must assun that they swim back to their spawnir grounds at a certain depth. Their larg reserves of fat must provide sustenance f the journey and for the build-up of t sexual products. Silver eels can live for to 4 years in an aquarium without feedin

If, as is believed, they spawn in t

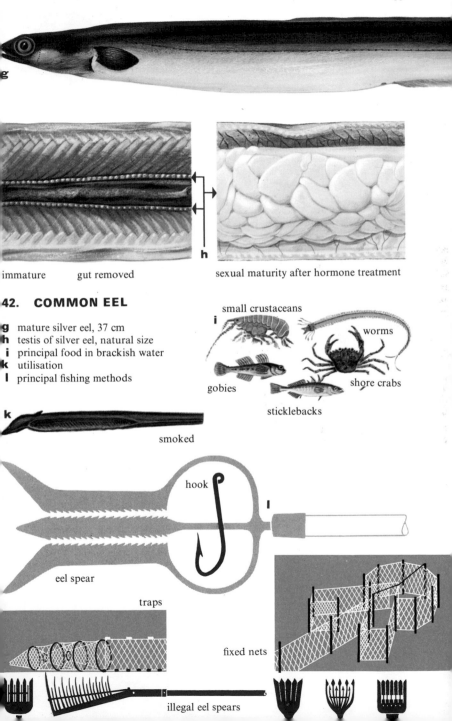

immature   gut removed

sexual maturity after hormone treatment

42. COMMON EEL

g mature silver eel, 37 cm
h testis of silver eel, natural size
i principal food in brackish water
k utilisation
l principal fishing methods

small crustaceans

worms

gobies

shore crabs

sticklebacks

smoked

hook

eel spear

traps

fixed nets

illegal eel spears

Sargasso Sea during the following spring they must travel *c*. 30 km per day; however, it is not known whether they spend a year longer on the journey. It is, however, certain that they die after spawning.

If eels are prevented from moving into the sea they may reach an age of 25–50 years. The external differences between yellow and silver eels are so striking that they were formerly regarded as separate species.

Yellow eels are caught in seines, traps, by hooks and line and with eel spears, the silver eels in traps and fixed eel nets, during their migration to the sea. The Baltic Sea eels have to pass through the narrow Danish coastal waters in order to reach the Atlantic, so the eel fishery there is especially

eel landing net

rewarding. Eels can be easily kept in fish boxes and dispatched alive. They are very hardy. The external gill openings are very small and therefore the sensitive gills do not so easily become desiccated, so eels can even survive for some time out of water. Their thick, slimy skin also protects them from desiccation.

Eels are marketed fresh, smoked and salted, and in southern Europe the elvers are canned.

The main countries fishing eels are Denmark (4,000–5,000 tons), Holland (3,000 tons), Italy (2,000–3,000 tons), Sweden (2,000 tons), France (1,000 tons), Poland (1,000 tons), Britain (600–800 tons), Norway, Spain and Germany (each *c*. 500 tons).

43. Conger eel

Conger conger (L.)

The conger differs from the common eel in the extent of the dorsal fin which starts above the tips of the pectoral fins. The skin is scaleless and the upper jaw extends beyond the lower jaw.

The males are *c*. 1 m long, the females 1·5–2 m. Maximum length 3 m (65 kg). Conger eels live mainly in rocky coastal waters in depths of 0–100 m. They are voracious predators that feed on herring, cod, lobsters, crawfish and cuttlefish.

They become sexually mature at an age of 5–15 years. During the breeding period the alimentary canal and other organs degenerate, the teeth fall out and the skeleton becomes decalcified. At the same time the gonads increase enormously in size, so that just before spawning they probably account for a third of the body weight.

Conger eels spawn in summer in an area that extends from the Sargasso Sea to the eastern Mediterranean, with depths of 2,000–3,000 m, but we do not know the actual depths in which spawning takes

3. CONGER EEL

a

Conger conger

- 122 cm
- larva, 14 cm
- principal food
- principal fishing method

b

crustaceans fishes

cuttlefishes

c

d

hook

place. Number of eggs: 3–8 million. The adults die after spawning.

For 1–2 years the larvae live a pelagic existence in depths of 100–200 m, and when 14–16 cm long they change into the typical eel shape, losing some length in so doing, and move to the coasts where they live close to the bottom. In contrast to the common eel they are never found in fresh water.

Young congers grow very rapidly. In an aquarium they have reached a weight of 40 kg in 5 years.

Congers are caught by long line. They do some damage to the fisheries as they take fish from the nets and also enter lobster pots. Their flesh is coarse.

Congers are landed in France (6,000 tons), Spain (4,000 tons), Portugal (?) and Britain (1,000 tons).

44. Garfish

Belone belone (L.)

Length *c*. 70 cm at 3–4 years (1 kg). Maximum length 90 cm. Pelagic shoaling fishes which mostly live close to the surface, and have a migratory pattern similar to that of the mackerel.

From the eastern Atlantic they reach the British Isles in March-April, the North Sea and Kattegat in April-May. The main spawning period is in May-June, but may extend into September. The number of eggs varies from 1,000 to 35,000, depending upon the size of the female. The eggs, which are probably laid in batches, have a diameter of 3–3·5 mm, and 60–80 long, sticky filaments by which they adhere to plants and rocks. They hatch in 5 weeks into young fish that are 13 mm long, but do not yet have the long snout. During the course of their further development the lower jaw at first grows faster than the upper jaw.

The young fish keep close to the coasts and feed on various small invertebrates, such as copepods. They reach a length of about 25 cm in the first year, and after a further year they will be about 45 cm long and sexually mature. They grow considerably slower in the Black Sea. Garfish live for up to 18 years.

After spawning the adults become widely distributed and hunt small herring, sprats, sand-eels, sticklebacks and crustaceans. They feed by eye, and mainly by day.

In the latter part of the year the garfish return to the waters to the west and south of the British Isles. Similar spawning and feeding migrations occur in the Mediterranean and Black Sea.

Garfish are excellent swimmers which often leap high up above the water surface when chased by tunny and dolphins. They are mostly caught in fixed nets and on drifting long lines that are supported by floats at the surface. The flesh is relatively dry, but fattest in autumn. They are not particularly popular as food on account of the green skeleton. This colour is, however, due to a completely harmless pigment.

About 5,000–7,000 tons are caught in European waters: Denmark (*c*. 2,200 tons), Spain (1,500 tons) and Italy (1,000 tons).

44. GARFISH

Belone belone

a 70 cm
b eggs × *c.* 6
c larvae × *c.* 4
d longitudinal section
e principal food
f principal fishing methods

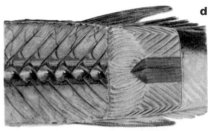

green skeleton

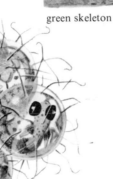

eggs attached to sea-grass, shortly before
hatching into larva (3–3½ mm)

c

at 13 mm

up to 45 mm

sand-eels

small herring

f

hooks

fixed nets

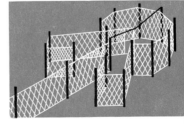

a

45. SKIPPER OR SAURY

Scomberesox saurus (Walbaum)

a 40 cm
b principal food
c principal fishing methods
Body taller and more laterally compressed
than that of the garfish. Easily recognised
by the row of small fins behind the dorsal
and anal fins. In contrast to garfish, the
skeleton is not green.

pelagic crustaceans   small fishes

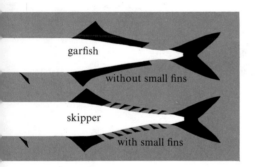

pelagic crustaceans, and also on small fish.
They often leap clear of the water, particularly when chased by tunny and other
enemies. During the summer the shoals
move northwards and are sometimes even
found in the Barents Sea. They are caught
in drift nets and on hooks, but are of little
economic importance.

Maximum length *c.* 50 cm. Skippers are
pelagic shoaling fishes that live out in the
open sea, close to the surface. The eggs are
also pelagic (diameter 2 mm) but have
shorter filaments than those of garfish.
They spawn in the open sea. The larvae
lack the long snout which only develops
during the course of further growth, as in
the garfish. The rate of development of the
two jaws is, however, more equal.

Skippers feed on euphausians and other

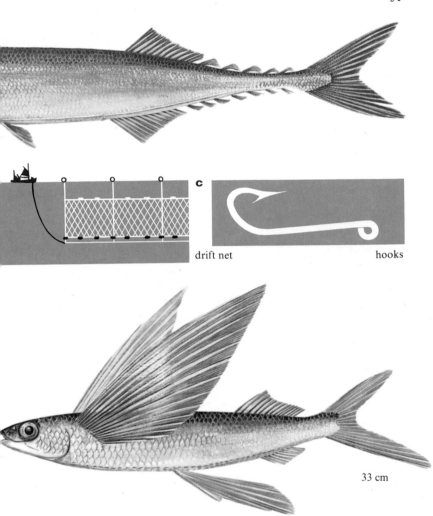

drift net   hooks

33 cm

FLYING FISHES

These are tropical and subtropical relatives of the garfish and skipper. They are able to propel themselves out of the water by rapid and powerful strokes of the tail and then to glide using the broad pectoral fins; a 'flight' may last *c*. 10 seconds and cover a distance of up to 100 m. One species *Cypsilurus heterurus* has strayed a couple of times as far as Oslo Fjord.

PIPEFISHES

Elongated thin fishes, in which the body is covered with a bony outer skeleton. Snout long and tubular, working as a pipette to catch small prey. The male carries the eggs until they hatch. Live mainly among seaweeds.

Key

1 {
With pectoral fins and caudal fin **2**
Without pectorals and caudal fin **4**

2 {
Snout more than ½ as tall as head .... **Broad-nosed pipefish**, p. 93
Snout less than ½ head height **3**

3 {
18–19 body rings between head and dorsal fin .... **Great pipefish**, p. 93
13–15 body rings between head and dorsal fin .... **Nilsson's pipefish**, p. 93

4 {
Anal opening below rear end of dorsal fin .... **Snake pipefish**, p. 94
Anal opening below front end of dorsal fin **5**

5 {
Snout curving upwards.......................... **Worm pipefish**, p. 95
Snout straight .... **Straight-nosed pipefish**, p. 94

---

46. Broad-nosed pipefish

Syngnathus typhle L.

Maximum length 30 cm. A non-migratory fish of the seaweed zone, in shallow water. Spawns in summer. The female produces 100–250 eggs which she transfers, using her elongated genital papilla, into the brood pouch of the male where they are fertilised. The male's brood pouch is a longish structure on the underside of the body, formed by two folds of skin. It can accommodate 50–100 eggs, and is sometimes used by several females.

The eggs, which have a diameter of *c*. 1·7 mm, are surrounded by the soft tissue of the brood pouch. They hatch in 4 weeks into young that are fully developed miniatures of the parents. These become sexually mature in one year and live for 2–3 years. They feed mainly on small crustaceans and fish fry.

47. Nilsson's pipefish

Syngnathus rostellatus Nilsson

Maximum length 17 cm. Lives among seaweeds in shallow coastal waters; its habits are similar to those of the previous species. Spawns in summer, the eggs having a diameter of 1 mm, and the newly hatched young a length of 13–14 mm.

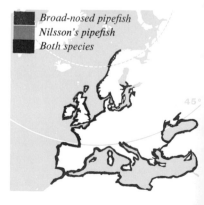

Broad-nosed pipefish
Nilsson's pipefish
Both species

male, 18 cm

46. BROAD-NOSED PIPEFISH *Syngnathus typhle*

female, 14 cm

47. NILSSON'S PIPEFISH *Syngnathus rostellatus*

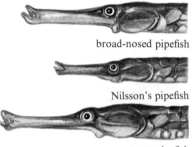

broad-nosed pipefish

Nilsson's pipefish

great pipefish

principal food of pipefishes

copepods

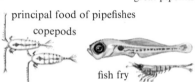

fish fry

48. GREAT PIPEFISH

Syngnathus acus (L.)

Male, 37 cm, with brood pouch containing young

Maximum length 46 cm. Males larger than females. Live among seaweeds. Spawn in spring or summer. The female transfers 200–400 eggs (diameter 2·4 mm) into the male's brood pouch. These hatch in 5 weeks into young that are 30 mm long.

49. SNAKE PIPEFISH

Entelurus aequoreus (L.)

The females reach a length of 45–60 cm, the males 32–40 cm. Live in depths of 5–100 m. A female lays 400–1,000 eggs (diameter 1·2 mm) which she transfers to the underside of several males during June-July. The newly hatched young are 11–12 mm long and have pectoral fins which, however, regress during the course of further development. Diet: fish fry and small crustaceans.

Sea-horses belong to the same group as the pipefishes

50. STRAIGHT-NOSED PIPEFISH

Nerophis ophidion (L.)

The females grow to 30 cm, the males t 25 cm. Inhabitants of the seaweed zone i depths of 2–15 m. Spawning takes place i May-August when the female produce 200–300 eggs with a diameter of 1 mm Each male may carry 50–200 eggs on hi belly until they hatch into young (9 mm Diet: small crustaceans, fish fry. Longevit *c.* 3 years.

■ Straight-nosed pipefish
▨ Worm pipefish
■ Both species

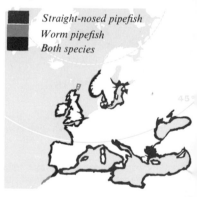

51. WORM PIPEFISH

Nerophis lumbriciformis (Jenyns)

Females reach a length of 17 cm, mal 14 cm. Live in shallow coastal region Spawn in the summer months, and th males carry 60–90 eggs (diameter 1–1 mm) on their belly until they hatch int young fish (9 mm). Diet: fish fry, sma crustaceans.

female, 46 cm

head, × c. 3

female, 26 cm

51. WORM PIPEFISH

Nerophis lumbriciformis

male, 12 cm

74 cm

52. GRENADIER

Coryphaenoides rupestris Gunnerus

Similar in body form to the rabbitfishes. Large, spiny scales. Body plump with a short, broad snout.

Maximum length 1 m. Living on the bottom in depths of 100–800 m. Spawning takes place in autumn (August-October), the female laying 12,000–16,000 pelagic eggs (diameter 1·8 mm). Diet: mainly deep-sea prawns. Caught on hooks and in prawn trawls, but of no economic importance.

The grenadiers or rat-tails form a group of about 120 species in the Atlantic and Pacific Oceans in depths of 100–500 m, of which 4–5 species occur in the north-east Atlantic; they are related to the cod group.

general view

Portuguese Dory fishery, Newfoundland

THE COD GROUP

The members of this group have soft fin rays and three, two or one dorsal fins. The ventral fins on the throat, in front of the pectoral fins. Most species have a barbel on the chin which serves as a sense organ when searching for food. These barbels, and also those on tip of the snout in rockling, have a rich supply of sensory cells.

These fishes live in cold and temperate seas and only a few species occur in fresh water. They prefer waters with a high salinity and, with the exception of the cod, only occur as strays in the brackish waters of the Baltic Sea.

Most species live in the waters close to the bottom, often just above it. Whiting, blue whiting, saithe and Norway pout also occur in the upper waters of the open water.

The females lay large numbers of pelagic eggs, even up to several millions. The fry feed mainly on plankton, before moving down towards the bottom. The adults feed principally on crustaceans, worms, molluscs and echinoderms. When old the large species (cod, ling) feed almost exclusively on other fish species.

In addition to the typical species with three dorsal fins (see identification key opposite) the following fishes also belong to the cod group: lesser and greater forkbeards (p. 112), ling (p. 115), hake (p. 116) and the rocklings (p. 118).

Landings of cod and related species amount to about 10 million tons a year or 17% of the world's fishery yield. This is only exceeded by the landings of herring, but these are of considerably lower market value. The principal countries taking part in the cod fishery are the Soviet Union, Great Britain, Norway, Japan and Canada. These countries land a total of about 7·5 million tons a year. The catches are mostly made with trawl and long line. The different species of the group are marketed fresh, sometimes filleted, or smoked; in northern countries the preparation of 'klipfisk' and stockfish is also of considerable importance (see p. 230). An oil produced from cod liver is used medically. The roe is also marketed separately, often smoked, and is used as a bait for sardines.

Key for the identification of fishes of the cod group with 3 dorsal fins

Lower jaw protruding **2**
Upper jaw protruding **6**

Upperside of head with 7 open mucus grooves............. **Silvery pout,** p. 113
Upperside of head without mucus grooves **3**

Dorsal fins clearly separated from one
another **4**

Dorsal fins close to one another **5**

Anus in front of 1st dorsal fin .... **Blue whiting,** p. 109

Anus behind 1st dorsal fin .... **Polar cod,** p. 103

Barbels small; unpaired fins with concave
rear edges; snout shorter than eye diameter **Norway pout,**
p. 109

With or without small barbels; lateral line
pale, almost straight; snout longer than
eye diameter .... **Saithe,** p. 111

Without barbels; lateral line curved; snout
longer than eye diameter; lower jaw
protruding .... **Pollack,** p. 110

Eye diameter less than snout length **7**

Eye diameter about same as snout length **8**

With black spot below 1st dorsal fin ....
Haddock, p. 105

With black spot at pectoral fin base ....
Whiting, p. 107

Without a black spot at pectoral fin base;
barbel long............................ **Cod,** p. 99

Anus below rear end of 1st dorsal fin ....
Poor-cod, p. 107

Anus below centre of 1st dorsal fin; with a
black spot at pectoral fin base .... **Bib,** p. 105

53. Cod

Gadus morrhua L.

With a protruding upper jaw, a well-developed barbel on the chin and a pale lateral line. The ground colour varies according to the habitat; reddish or brownish in the algal zone, greenish when among eel-grass, and pale grey on a sandy bottom or in deeper waters. Specimens with a length of 110 cm and a weight of 15 kg are frequently caught in Icelandic waters and off the Lofotens, their age being *c*. 20 years. Rarely more than 150 cm and up to weights of 40 kg. Cod occur from coastal waters down to depths of 500–600 m, mainly at temperatures of 2–10°C, usually near the bottom but also pelagic. Some of the large cod (15–20 years old) apparently move far out into the open sea, where they hunt herring and other shoaling fishes.

Like the herring, cod also form races with different spawning habits, rates of growth and preferred areas. The most important stocks are oceanic, migratory fish which undertake extensive spawning and feeding migrations. Of these the most important to the fisheries are the Norwegian-Arctic cod stock in the Barents Sea, the Icelandic stock and the populations off Greenland and Newfoundland. The forms in the North and Baltic Seas account for only 10 per cent or less of the total stock. In addition to these large, far-ranging stocks, there are also local, stationary races which always remain close inshore.

Most populations spawn in the spring, and for this they move into waters with a temperature of 4–6°C. The number of eggs laid varies, according to the size of the female, between 500,000 and 5 million. The eggs and sperm are released into the open sea as the male and female come close together. The transparent eggs, 1·5 mm in diameter, are pelagic and within a short time they rise to the surface. They hatch in 2–4 weeks, according to the temperature. The newly hatched young are *c*. 5 mm long and, as long as they remain pelagic, feed on copepods and other small planktonic animals. After 3–5 months the young are

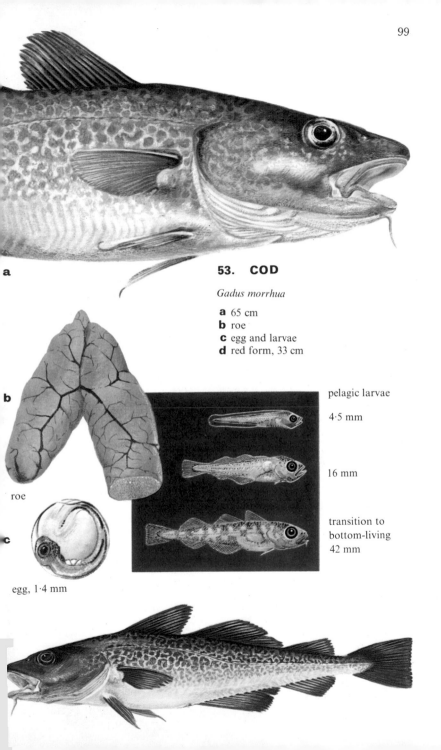

53. COD

Gadus morrhua

a 65 cm
b roe
c egg and larvae
d red form, 33 cm

b

roe

c

egg, 1·4 mm

pelagic larvae

4·5 mm

16 mm

transition to
bottom-living
42 mm

3–6 cm long and they now move down to the bottom. The young of the oceanic cod stocks move into relatively deep water, those of the coastal forms into shallow water. The pelagic eggs and larvae are subject to the currents and are often driven far from their parents' spawning grounds.

During the following years the growth rate of the young fish is dependent upon the water temperature, the density of the shoal (food competition) and the amount and quality of the available food supply. Cod are omnivorous, feeding on all kinds of crustaceans, worms and molluscs, and with increasing age on other fish. Those that are migratory follow the spawning movements of herring and capelin; sand-eels are also an important food. During the spawning period of the herring, cod are often caught with their stomachs full of herring roe. On the other hand, cod eat far less in the winter months and also during their own spawning period.

The large migratory stocks of cod off Newfoundland, Greenland, Iceland and Norway become sexually mature at an age of 6–15 years, usually at 8–12 years when they are 70–100 cm long and weigh 3–8 kg. Coastal cod grow more rapidly and in Danish waters they are mature at 2 years, off western Norway at 4–6 years.

The immature Arctic-Norwegian cod in the Barents Sea are known as 'capelin cod'. They follow the spawning movements of the capelin and in April-June they arrive in vast shoals off the coast of Finnmark where they are fished as 'spring cod'. When mature they are known in Norwegian as 'skrei'. During the autumn these fish move from the Barents Sea to the Lofotens, arriving at their spawning grounds in January-February. The main spawning takes place in the transition layers between the cold coastal water and the underlying, warmer Atlantic water, usually in depths of 80 cm. In April they return with the northward currents to the Barents Sea. From then on the mature fish take part every year in the spawning migration.

Icelandic cod spawn off the south-west coast of Iceland, and their habits are similar to those of the Arctic-Norwegian stock. Tagging experiments have shown that they migrate long distances and even reach the Barents Sea and west Greenland.

Greenlandic cod are derived from the Icelandic stock and periodically considerable exchanges take place between these two populations. Off Greenland they spawn at 4°C in depths of 200–450 m on the steep slopes of the Davis Strait.

Cod are caught by trawls and Danish seines (on even bottoms), with set gill nets, drift nets, purse seines and long lines (when the fish are close to the surface or the bottom is rough). Coastal cod are also caught in traps and fixed nets. When catching 'skrei cod' the bait must be carefully chosen because these fish eat very little during the spawning period. Lightly salted mussels (transported in barrels) are frequently used.

The 'spring cod' fishery off Finnmark and the 'skrei' fishery off Lofoten are both of great economic importance.

In Icelandic waters, bank line fishing is carried out on their spawning grounds off the Westmann Islands in March-April and off the north and east coasts in summer.

As a result of the warming up of the arctic, cod have spread into Greenlandic waters since about 1920.

In comparison with the great fisheries in northern waters, the catch in the North and Baltic Seas is very poor. The North Sea Convention has fixed the minimum size to be caught at 30 cm.

The Scandinavian word for cod is 'torsk', which means 'dry fish'. Since Viking times dried cod has been an important basic food and article of trade for the northern nations, both in the form of stockfish (dried) and klipfisk (split, salted and dried). Coastal cod are also marketed alive or freshly iced. A large quantity is filleted and deep-frozen.

Cod offal is processed into fish meal. At least 60,000 tons of cod liver oil is produced every year. The roe is marketed fresh or salted, and a considerable quantity is used as bait in the pilchard fishery.

The total annual catch in the North

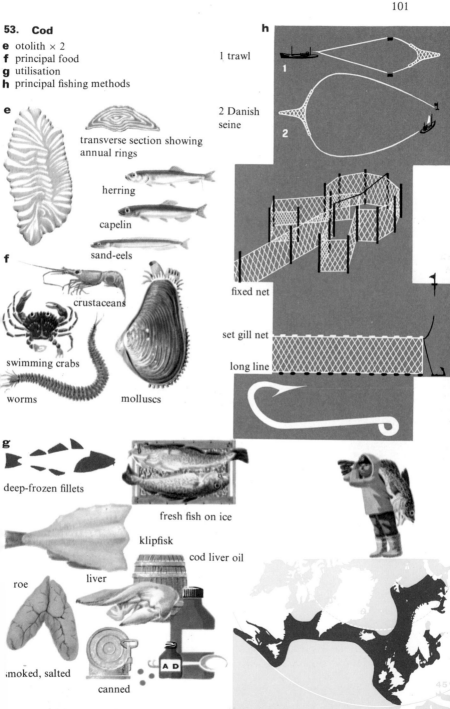

53. Cod

e otolith × 2
f principal food
g utilisation
h principal fishing methods

h

1 trawl

2 Danish seine

e

transverse section showing annual rings

herring

capelin

sand-eels

f

crustaceans

swimming crabs

molluscs

worms

fixed net

set gill net

long line

g

deep-frozen fillets

fresh fish on ice

klipfisk

cod liver oil

roe

liver

smoked, salted

canned

A D

Atlantic is *c*. 2·5 million tons. Of this Norway takes 400,000–500,000 tons, Great Britain 300,000–400,000 tons, Canada, Iceland, Spain, and the Soviet Union 200,000–300,000 tons each, France, Germany, and Portugal 100,000–200,000 tons each, Denmark and Poland 90,000–130,000 tons each, Faeroes 60,000–80,000 tons, Holland 20,000–50,000 tons, Sweden 25,000 tons, Belgium 15,000–25,000 tons, Greenland 20,000 tons, Ireland 3,000–4,000 tons. There is a close relative of the Atlantic cod in the northern part of the Pacific Ocean.

Ogac or **Greenland cod,** *Gadus ogac,* is also a close relative, possibly only a special coastal form of the Atlantic cod.

It differs in having a marbled body coloration, a broad head and a somewhat stouter body. The lateral line is darker, with coarse scales and pores. This form reaches a length of *c*. 50 cm at 5–6 years, and is rarely more than 60 cm long and 9 years old. The Greenland cod lives in the fjords and coastal waters of Greenland, at depths of 1–200 m, spawning in shallow water in February-May. The ovary is surrounded by a thin, blackish membrane. The eggs sink to the bottom. Like the ordinary cod this is an omnivorous fish.

At one time the Greenland cod was very abundant in the coastal waters of Greenland, but during recent decades its numbers have seriously declined; it has possibly been displaced by the common cod.

It is of no economic importance, being too lean to produce good salt fish.

54. Polar cod

Boreogadus saida (Lepechin)

Lower jaw protruding with a small barbel.

Body very slender. Anus below the front end of the second dorsal fin.

Sexually mature at a length of *c*. 20 cm and an age of 4 years. Seldom more than *c*. 25 cm and 7 years. Maximum length 40 cm.

These are pelagic fish living near the surface at temperatures below 5°C, often in the drift ice and along the edge of the pack ice. They can evidently tolerate brackish water, so are often found in estuaries. In winter they move further south and spawn near the coast at a temperature of 1–0°C. The female produces 9,000–18,000 pelagic eggs which hatch in April-May. Both the larvae and the adult fish feed on planktonic organisms. Polar cod are themselves eaten by common cod, seals, arctic toothed whales and sea birds.

Because the arctic has become warmer in recent times, the Polar cod like many other arctic animals are able to penetrate further north. The species was formerly very common in the coastal waters of southern Greenland.

Polar cod are caught when on their spawning migrations, particularly by the Soviet Union. The flesh and liver are used

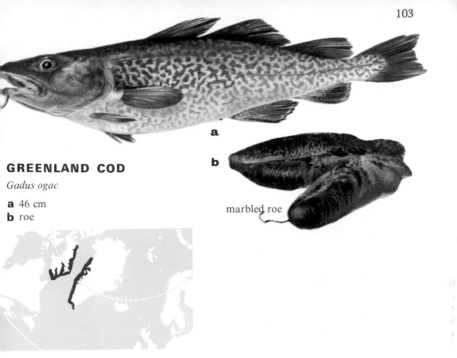

GREENLAND COD
Gadus ogac

a 46 cm
b roe

marbled roe

28 cm

54. POLAR COD
Boreogadus saida

55. Haddock

Melanogrammus aeglefinus (L.)

Easily recognised by the large black spot above the pectoral fin. Lateral line black.

Sexually mature in the North Sea at a length of 30–40 cm and age of 3–4 years, off northern Norway at 40–65 cm and 4–8 years. Maximum length 1 m (weight 12 kg). Longevity *c.* 20 years.

Haddock live close to the bottom in depths of 10–200 m at 4–10°C. During the winter months the sexually mature fish move to their spawning grounds: northern North Sea, off Trondheim and Møre in Norway, off south-west Iceland and the Faeroes. They spawn in March-June in places with a high salinity, at a temperature of 5–7°C and in depths of 50–150 m. The female produces 100,000–1 million transparent, pelagic eggs which rise to the surface. After 1–3 weeks (varying according to the temperature) these hatch into larvae (*c.* 5 mm long) which are distributed widely by the currents; at a length of 5–10 cm they move down to the bottom, usually into relatively deep water. At one year of age they are 15–18 cm long.

Haddock feed on brittlestars, molluscs, worms, herring and capelin eggs and young fish. Within the distribution range the rate of growth is very variable. They are caught in trawls and seines and by long line. The most important fishing grounds are in the North Sea and Barents Sea, off Iceland and off the east coast of North America. The North Sea population shows all the signs of overfishing. The North Sea Convention has laid down the minimum size to be caught as 27 cm. In the Barents Sea haddock (usually 3–9 years old, 35–75 cm long) are caught in May-November.

Haddock are not landed alive, and most of the catch is marketed as fresh fish on ice or as deep-frozen fillets; also smoked, particularly in Britain.

The total annual European catch is *c.* 500,000 tons, of which Britain takes 100,000–200,000 tons, the Soviet Union *c.* 80,000 tons, Norway 40,000–60,000 tons, Denmark and Iceland 30,000–35,000

tons each, France 10,000–18,000 tons, Faeroes 7,000–13,000 tons, Germany and Holland 6,000–11,000 tons each.

The North American catches are Canada 25,000–50,000 tons. U.S.A. 10,000–20,000 tons.

56. Bib

Trisopterus luscus (L.)

Distinctive features: Upper jaw somewhat protruding; long barbel; large eyes (diameter as long as snout length). Anus lying below the middle of the first dorsal fin.

The bib or pout reaches a length of *c.* 30 cm, and lives at moderate depths in coastal waters, often over rocky ground; it feeds on crustaceans and small fishes. Spawns in spring. Not abundant in the northern and southern parts of its range. Of little economic importance, although Spain lands *c.* 3,000–6,000 tons annually.

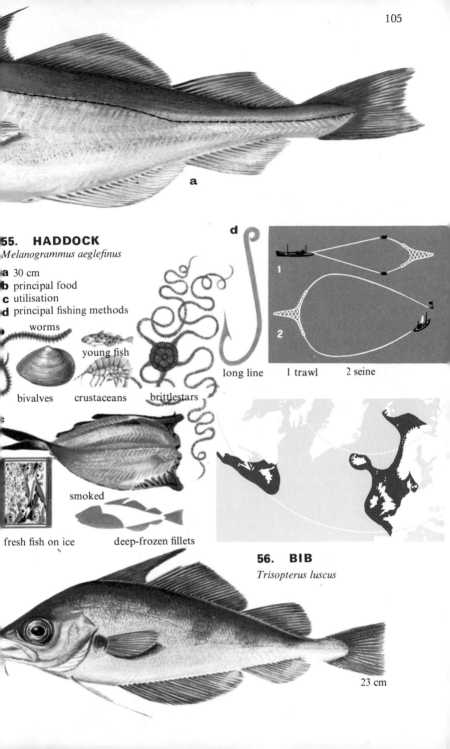

a

55. HADDOCK
Melanogrammus aeglefinus

a 30 cm
b principal food
c utilisation
d principal fishing methods

worms

young fish

bivalves   crustaceans   brittlestars

d

1 trawl   2 seine

long line

smoked

fresh fish on ice   deep-frozen fillets

56. BIB
Trisopterus luscus

23 cm

106

57. Poor-cod

Trisopterus minutus (L.)

Distinctive features: Upper jaw somewhat protruding; long barbel; large eyes (diameter greater than snout length). Anus below the rear end of first dorsal fin.

Poor-cod reach a length of 19–23 cm. They feed on crustaceans and small fishes in depths of 25–300 m, and spawn in February-June.

They are too small to be of any importance as human food, although they are often caught in the trawl, and are sometimes processed into fish meal.

58. Whiting

Merlangius merlangus (L.)

Distinctive features: Upper jaw protruding; no barbel on lower jaw; with a black spot at the base of the pectoral fin.

Whiting are about 20 cm long when 2 years old; in the North Sea they seldom exceed 40 cm, but off Iceland may be 40–50 cm, or even 70 cm long. They occur from the coastal eel-grass zone down to depths of 200 m.

They become sexually mature after 3–4 years and spawn between January and September. Most of the spawning takes place in early spring in depths of 30–100 m.

The larvae and young fish often live beneath the umbrella of a jellyfish, possibly to seek protection, but they may also eat the jellyfish eggs. During the pelagic period of their life they are widely distributed by sea currents. They do not move down to near the bottom until quite late, when they are 5–10 cm long.

Adult whiting feed on prawns, swimming-crabs and particularly on other fishes: small herring, sand-eels and Norway pout. They are popular sporting fish and are much angled for from piers and rocky coasts. In recent years the whiting has become quite important economically, and the annual landings total 150,000 tons. The main catch in the North Sea and in Scottish coastal waters is used for human consumption, but those caught off Ireland (c. 12,000 tons) and in the Kattegat-Skagerrak area (10,000–15,000 tons) are usually processed into fish meal.

Whiting are mainly caught in the trawl and also incidentally in herring and prawn nets. In the North Sea the minimum length that can be landed is 23 cm.

57. POOR-COD

Trisopterus minutus

20 cm

a

58. WHITING

Merlangius merlangus

a 25 cm
b young stages
c larva, 11 mm
d principal food
e utilisation
f principal fishing methods

deep-sea prawns

sand-eels

Norway pout

small herring

fish meal   fodder

deep-frozen fillets

fresh fish on ice

b

c

f

trawl

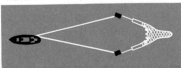

59. Blue whiting

Micromesistius poutassou (Risso)

Blue whiting

Characteristics: Mouth and gill cavity black. The first two dorsal fins are very short and far apart from one another. Lower jaw somewhat protruding, without a barbel.

The blue whiting reaches a length of 50 cm at the most, lives in depths of 80–300 m, feeds on crustaceans and small fishes and spawns in early spring. The young are pelagic until about 15 cm long; the adults also live mainly in the open sea.

This species is caught incidentally in prawn trawls, and used for fish meal.

60. Norway pout

Trisopterus esmarkii (Nilsson)

Characteristics: Lower jaw protruding, with a small barbel; eyes large (diameter greater than snout length). The anus lies below the gap between the first and second dorsal fins. All the unpaired fins have a slightly concave rear edge.

Norway pout reach a length of 9–13 cm in their first year, 14–19 cm in their second. Maximum length *c.* 25 cm. In most parts of their range they live in depths of 80–300 m, but in the Skagerrak and eastern Kattegat they may be in depths less than 40 m.

Spawning takes place in January-March in the northern North Sea, north of Scotland, off the Orkneys, Shetlands and Faeroes, to the north of Ireland and in the Skagerrak-Kattegat area.

This species apparently undertakes extensive migrations. The populations off the Faeroes and in the northern Kattegat are evidently isolated and have their own spawning grounds. Norway pout are usually sexually mature at an age of 2 years. However, off the Shetlands and in northern Scotland (Moray Firth) a pro

portion of the one year old fish are sexually mature.

This is the most abundant species within the cod group, and although they are no suitable for human consumption o account of their small size, they ar indirectly of great importance to th fishing industry as they are eaten by had dock, whiting, cod and hake. They them selves feed on euphausians and smal fishes.

They are mainly caught in trawls by th Danes and processed into fish meal.

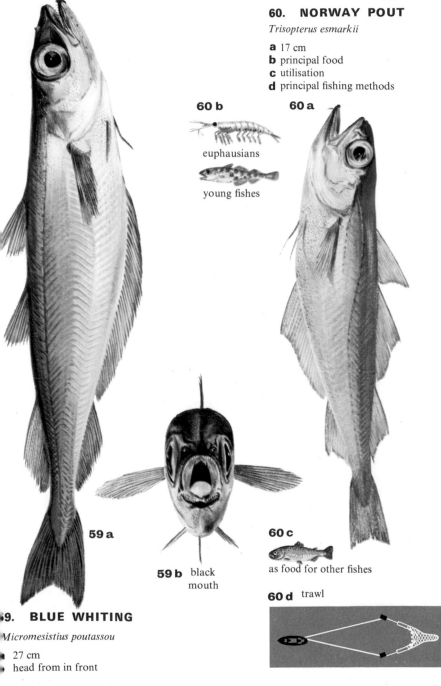

60. NORWAY POUT

Trisopterus esmarkii

a 17 cm
b principal food
c utilisation
d principal fishing methods

60 b

euphausians

young fishes

60 a

59 a

59 b black mouth

60 c

as food for other fishes

60 d trawl

59. BLUE WHITING

Micromesistius poutassou

27 cm
head from in front

40 cm

61. POLLACK

Pollachius pollachius (L.)

Characteristics: Lower jaw protruding, without a barbel. Lateral line above the pectoral fins curved towards the back. Anus below the front half of the first dorsal fin.

Reaches a length of *c.* 1 m and lives pelagically or close to the bottom, from near the coasts down to depths of 200 m. Feeds on deep-sea prawns, sand-eels, herring and sprats. Spawns to the east and south of the British Isles, in the northern North Sea and off southern Norway.

The flesh is dry but of good flavour.

Pollack are caught along with cod in gill nets, traps and by long line. The total annual European catch is *c.* 6,000 tons, of which Norway lands *c.* 2,000 tons.

62. Saithe

Pollachius virens (L.)

Characteristics: Lower jaw protruding, barbels small or lacking. Lateral line pale, almost straight. Anus below the rear end of the first dorsal fin.

Maximum length 130 cm at *c.* 27 years, and reaching 60–70 cm in the 5th year.

Lives almost exclusively as a pelagic fish, in great depths and also near the surface.

Saithe or coalfish spawn in depths of 100–200 m, in places with a high salinity and a temperature of 6–8°C. After the pelagic larval stage the young fish live for their first 3–4 years in shallow water. They become sexually mature at 5–10 years.

Pollack

The young feed on copepods, euphausians and fish fry—including that of their own species. Adult saithe are very voracious predators which hunt herring, sprats and various young fishes. They are found in large numbers in areas where herring are caught, and are typical shoaling fish. Tagging experiments have shown that saithe undertake extensive migrations and often follow the spawning migrations of the herring over long distances. After their feeding migrations during the summer months they move to the spawning grounds at the onset of the cold weather. The total annual European catch is *c.* 400,000–600,000 tons, of which 100,000–160,000 tons are landed in Norway, *c.* 150,000 tons in the Soviet Union, *c.* 90,000 tons in Germany, 60,000 tons in Britain, 50,000–80,000 tons in France, 60,000 tons in Iceland. On the American side of the Atlantic, Canada takes 12,000 tons. The highest catches come in summer

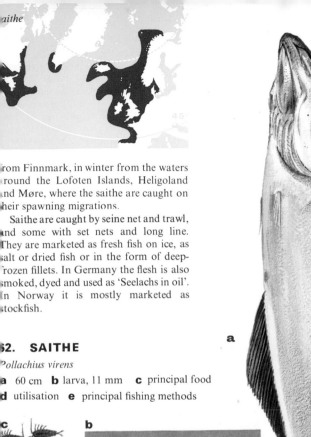

from Finnmark, in winter from the waters
round the Lofoten Islands, Heligoland
and Møre, where the saithe are caught on
their spawning migrations.

Saithe are caught by seine net and trawl,
and some with set nets and long line.
They are marketed as fresh fish on ice, as
salt or dried fish or in the form of deep-
frozen fillets. In Germany the flesh is also
smoked, dyed and used as 'Seelachs in oil'.
In Norway it is mostly marketed as
stockfish.

62. SAITHE

Pollachius virens

a 60 cm **b** larva, 11 mm **c** principal food
d utilisation **e** principal fishing methods

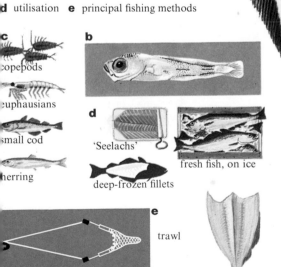

c

copepods

euphausians

small cod

herring

b

d

'Seelachs'

deep-frozen fillets

fresh fish, on ice

e

trawl

seine net

stockfish

long line

63. Silvery pout

Gadiculus argenteus thori Schmidt

Characteristics: Mouth facing obliquely upwards. No barbel on the lower jaw. Eyes large. The lateral line branches on the head end in 7 mucus grooves. Scales large, silvery and easily detached.

The smallest species of the cod group in the north-east Atlantic. Length 10–15 cm. Lives in depths of 60–1,000 m, but mainly in 100–300 m over muddy ground. Spawns in spring at considerable depths. Diet: worms and small crustaceans. Of no economic importance. A closely related form occurs off the west coast of Spain and in the Mediterranean.

64. Tadpole-fish

Raniceps raninus (L.)

Characteristics: First dorsal fin reduced to 3 short rays. Second dorsal fin and anal fin both long. Head broad and flat. With a small barbel on the lower jaw. The body shaped like a tadpole and is deep black covered with a thick shiny layer of mucu

Length *c.* 20 cm. Lives on the bottom mainly over rocky or stony ground in th seaweed belt. The tadpole-fish or lesse forkbeard seldom occurs in depths greate than 100 m. Spawning takes place in May September and the young fish move dow to the bottom in coastal areas when *c.* 2 cm long. These fish do not form shoals but liv solitarily and are never very numerous Diet: sea-stars, crustaceans, worms gobies. Of no economic importance.

65. Greater Forkbeard

Phycis blennioides (Brünnich)

Characteristics: Ventral fins long and fila mentous, reaching the front edge of the anal fin. First dorsal fin ending in a point Second dorsal fin and anal fin both long With a barb on the lower jaw.

Length: seldom over 60 cm, maximum 110 cm. Greater forkbeards live in shoals close to the bottom, in depths of 150–300 m, and feed on crustaceans and smal bottom-living fishes. Their biology ha been very little investigated, and it is no known whether they even spawn in the northern part of their range.

They are caught incidentally on long lines and in the trawl, and are used for fish meal. Greater forkbeards are, however, of more economic importance in the Mediterranean where they are landed in considerable numbers.

3. SILVERY POUT
...adiculus argenteus thori

14 cm

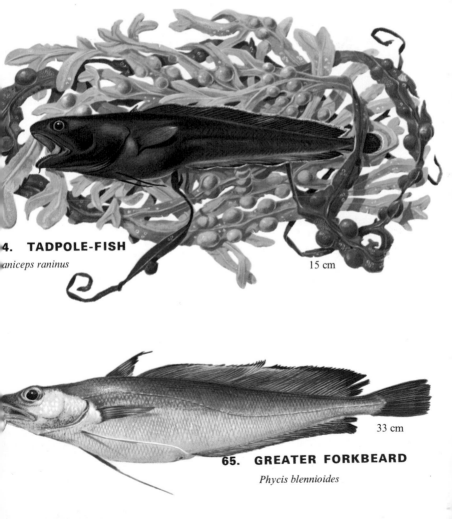

4. TADPOLE-FISH
...aniceps raninus

15 cm

33 cm

65. GREATER FORKBEARD
Phycis blennioides

LINGS

Characteristics: First dorsal fin short; second dorsal fin and anal fin long, but not fused with the caudal fin. Barbel on the lower jaw. Three species in Europe.

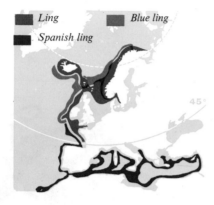

Ling Blue ling Spanish ling

group. Maximum weight *c*. 30 kg. Lives depths of 100–600 m, and spawns in Apr June, the female producing 20–60 milli pelagic eggs (diameter 1 mm) in depths 100–300 m off southern Iceland and in narrow belt along the 200 m depth conto between middle Norway and the Bay Biscay. Diet: blue whiting, Norway po gurnards and other fishes, Dublin B prawns and octopus.

Ling are caught on long lines and in t trawl. The total European catch is *c*. 50,0 tons a year, of which Norway lands 18,000 tons. Britain and Germany eac *c*. 7,000 tons, Sweden and Iceland eac *c*. 3,200 tons, and Belgium 1,000 tons. Norway, Scotland, Iceland and t Faeroes, ling is salted and dried to produ klipfisk which is exported to souther Europe. In Sweden the fish are stretche out between wooden sticks, dried ar marketed as 'Spillånga'. Also marketed fillets which may be smoked or fried.

66. Blue ling

Molva dypterygia (Pennant)

With a shorter barbel and larger eyes than ling. Length 1·5 m. Lives in depths of 200–1,500 m. The spawning grounds are over the edge of the European Continental Shelf south of Iceland and west of the Faeroes and the British Isles, in depths of *c*. 1,000 m. The populations off Norway are probably always reinforced by immigration from these areas. Spawning takes place in April-May.

Caught on long lines and the flesh is even more esteemed than that of the common ling. Blue ling accounts for approximately 5–10% (*c*. 2,000–4,000 tons) of the total European catch of ling.

68. Spanish ling

Molva macrophthalma (Rafinesque-Schmaltz)

Characteristics: Ventral fins long, reachir beyond the rear end of the pectoral fins.

Maximum length *c*. 90 cm. This is th smallest species in the genus *Molva* and even more slender than ling or blue ling. lives in depths of 200–1,500 m and spawr in the eastern Mediterranean and in narrow belt running from Gibraltar southern Ireland.

Of minor economic importance in th Mediterranean.

67. Ling

Molva molva (L.)

Barbel longer than the diameter of the eye. Reaches a length of up to 1·8 m and is therefore the largest species in the cod

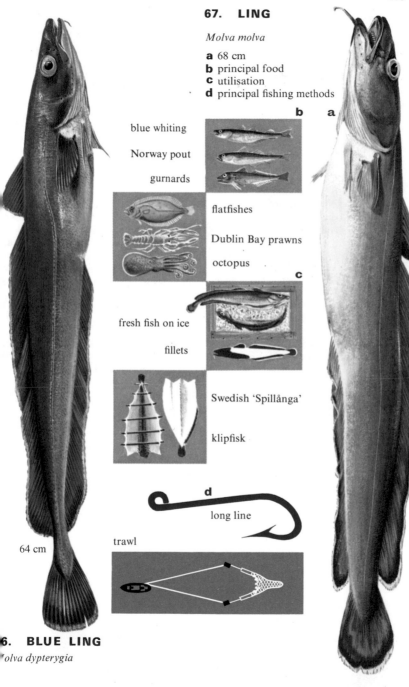

67. LING

Molva molva

a 68 cm
b principal food
c utilisation
d principal fishing methods

b   **a**

blue whiting

Norway pout

gurnards

flatfishes

Dublin Bay prawns

octopus

c

fresh fish on ice

fillets

Swedish 'Spillånga'

klipfisk

d

long line

trawl

64 cm

6. BLUE LING

olva dypterygia

69. Hake

Merluccius merluccius (L.)

Characteristics: First dorsal fin short, second dorsal and anal fins long. Lower jaw somewhat protruding, without a barbel. Mouth and gill cavity black.

Off France and the British Isles 4 year old hake are *c.* 33 cm long, but the rate of growth in the Mediterranean is considerably less. Seldom over 1 m long (10 kg). Lives in depths of 100–300 m, and spawns in March-June over the edge of the Continental Shelf south of Iceland and in the waters off France and the Iberian Peninsula. Lives near the bottom by day, but moves up during the night and hunts for herring, sprats, anchovies, pilchards and mackerel.

Hake are caught in the trawl and by long line. The total annual catch in Europe is 100,000–140,000 tons, of which Spain takes 65,000–100,000 tons, but 80% of this consists of young fish, 'pescadilla'. France 23,000 tons, Italy and Portugal each land 8,000–15,000 tons annually. Hake is marketed in the form of fillets or salted and dried. Small hake are also marketed fresh, and in Spain the roe is eaten fresh, dried or fried.

The North Sea Convention has laid down the minimum size to be caught as 30 cm. There are relatives of the hake in the waters off South Africa, North and South America which are caught in large numbers.

70. Torsk

Brosme brosme (Ascanius)

Characteristics: Only one long dorsal fin and one long anal fin, both being fused with the caudal fin. With a long barbel. Skin thick, with small scales.

Length 40–90 cm (2–10 kg). Torsk live close to the bottom in depths of 70–1,000 m, mostly over rocky ground in depths of 200–500 m. They become sexually mature when 8–10 years old and 40–50 cm long. Spawning takes place in April-June in depths of 200–500 m with a water temperature of 6–9°C. The female lays *c.* 2 million eggs (diameter 1·3–1·5 mm) which are pelagic. They hatch in about 10 days into larvae that are *c.* 4 mm long. The principal spawning grounds are south west of Iceland, off the Faeroes, north and west of Scotland. Diet: bottom-living fishes, Dublin Bay prawns and other large crustaceans.

Torsk are mainly caught in the trawl and on long lines. The total annual European catch is 25,000–30,000 tons of which Norway lands *c.* 20,000 tons, Iceland 4,000–5,000 tons, Britain *c.* 2,500 tons, Faeroes and Germany each *c.* 1,500 tons. In addition, this species is caught in Canadian waters, but is rare off Greenland. In the Nordic countries it is processed into stockfish, but in Germany it is mainly marketed in the form of fillets. The firm, white flesh has a flavour similar to that of lobster. The liver yields an oil rich in vitamins A and D.

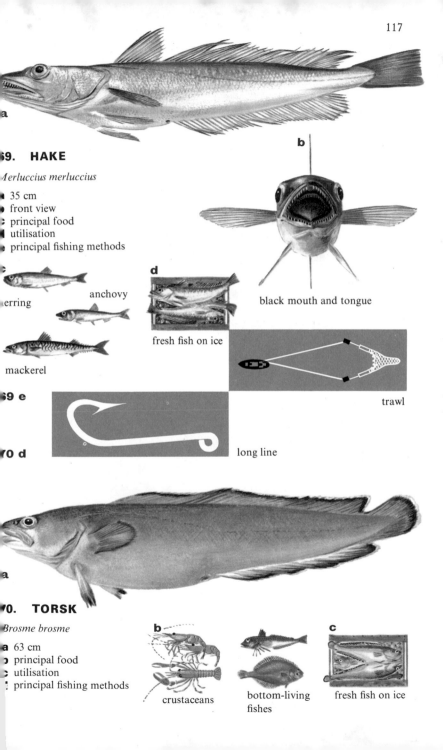

69. HAKE

Merluccius merluccius

a 35 cm
b front view
c principal food
d utilisation
e principal fishing methods

herring

anchovy

mackerel

black mouth and tongue

d fresh fish on ice

69 e

trawl

70 d

long line

70. TORSK

Brosme brosme

a 63 cm
b principal food
c utilisation
d principal fishing methods

crustaceans

bottom-living fishes

fresh fish on ice

118

ROCKLINGS

Belonging to the cod group, the rocklings have one barbel on the lower jaw and at least two on the snout. The first dorsal fin is much reduced and lies sunk in a longitudinal furrow on the back, with only the first fin ray protruding. The second dorsal fin and the anal fin are long.

sandy or rocky bottoms in the shallow water of the algal zone.

The eggs and larvae are pelagic. When about 3–4 cm long the young move down to live on the bottom.

Rocklings are widely distributed bottom-living fishes, but are not much caught. Their flesh is not particularly well flavoured.

71. Three-bearded rockling

Gaidropsarus vulgaris (Cloquet)

Characteristics: One barbel on the lower jaw and two on the snout. Maximum length 50–60 cm. Lives in depths of 0–250 m, but mainly in the shallow water of the algal zone. Feeds on crustaceans and small fishes, and spawns in summer.

Only of minor economic importance in certain areas.

72. Four-bearded rockling

Rhinonemus cimbrius (L.)

Characteristics: One barbel on the lower jaw and three on the snout. First ray of the dorsal fin considerably longer than in the other species.

Maximum length 30–40 cm. Lives in depths of 20–250 m, particularly on soft ground. Penetrates into the Baltic Sea and even spawns there.

Feeds on small crustaceans and spawns in February-August.

Of no economic value.

73. Five-bearded rockling

Ciliata mustela (L.)

Characteristics: One barbel on the lower jaw and four on the snout.

Maximum length 25–30 cm. Lives on

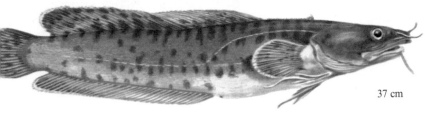

37 cm

1. THREE-BEARDED ROCKLING
Gaidropsarus vulgaris

a

2. FOUR-BEARDED ROCKLING
Rhinonemus cimbrius

a 22 cm
b head from in front

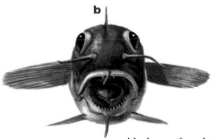

b

black mouth and tongue

young fish, 10 cm

3. FIVE-BEARDED ROCKLING
Ciliata mustela

50 cm

74. BERYX

Beryx decadactylus Cuvier

Belongs to a group of fishes which contains both so-called deep-sea fishes and also coralfishes in tropical and temperate seas.

This species reaches a length of up to 50 cm and lives pelagically in depths greater than 200 m. Rather rare in the northern North Sea and off Norway. The full range is not known, but it is probably larger than shown on the adjoining map.

B. splendens is a cosmopolitan relative with a more slender body.

75. DEALFISH

Trachypterus arcticus

75. Dealfish

Trachypterus arcticus (Brünnich)

Body much compressed and band-like. Maximum length *c.* 3 m. Lives pelagically in depths of 500–600 m. Sexually mature at a length of *c.* 2·4 m and an age of *c.* 14 years. The female lays half a million eggs. Rarely seen alive, but frequently washed up on the shores of the North Sea.

The ribbonfish, *Regalecus glesne,* reaches a length of up to 7 m. The first rays of the dorsal fin form a characteristic head plume, looking rather like a crown. Rarer than the dealfish, but washed up now and again on the coasts and is regarded as a good omen for a successful herring catch.

76. Opah

Lampris guttatus (Brünnich)

Body tall with strong lateral compression. Mouth small and toothless but can be protruded far forwards. The scales are small and come off easily when the fish is caught. The opah (or moonfish) belongs to the same group as the dealfish and ribbonfish.

Length 1·5–1·8 m, weight up to *c.* 100 kg. Lives pelagically in depths of 100–400 m and feeds mainly on squids. The opah has a cosmopolitan distribution, and is seen as a regular summer visitor in the northern North Sea and off western Norway. It is sometimes landed as an incidental catch in the herring fishery. The reddish, salmon-like flesh is very fatty. Its biology is almost completely unknown.

Beryx
Opah

Both species

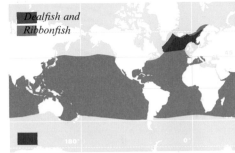

Dealfish and
Ribbonfish

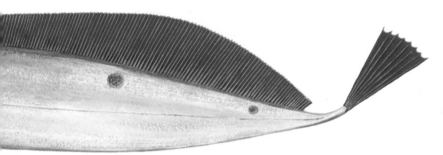

122 cm

76. OPAH

Lampris guttatus

a 95 cm
b principal food

b

squids

a

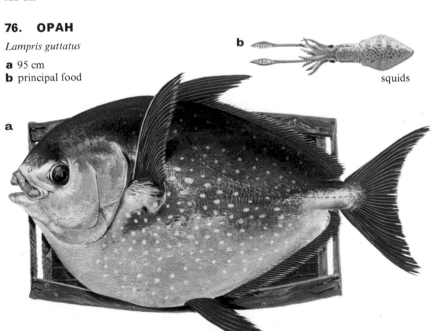

77. JOHN DORY

Zeus faber L.

a 37 cm
b larva, 8 mm

Body very tall and laterally compressed, mouth capable of being protruded far forwards. Average length 25–30 cm (2 kg), maximum length *c.* 60 cm (8 kg). Lives pelagically in small shoals or near the bottom in moderate depths. Spawns in June-August off the coasts of southern England, in March-May in the Mediterranean. The eggs are pelagic. After spawning some of the fish migrate out of the spawning area, whose limit runs north of the English Channel, into the North Sea and reach as far as south-western Norway and the Kattegat.

Feeds on pilchards, sprats and sandsmelts.

According to legend St Peter once drew a gold coin from the mouth of a John Dory, and even today one can see the apostle's fingerprints as a black mark, encircled with gold, on each side of the fish.

The term John Dory is probably derived from the Italian name for the fish: Janitore, the janitor.

John Dory has a particularly fine flavour. It forms a valuable incidental catch in the trawl and on long lines in the Mediterranean Sea and off the west coast of Africa. There are related species in the tropical and temperate zones of all the other oceans.

123

78. SCAD

Trachurus trachurus (L.)

Characterised by the large, keeled scales on the lateral line. About 25 cm long when 4 years old, maximum length 40 cm.

A pelagic, shoaling fish with similar habits to the mackerel. The female lays 3,000–139,000 pelagic eggs in November-March, but later in the North Sea (May-June). The young are often found in small shoals under jellyfishes.

Scad are of little economic importance in northern Europe. They are caught in the Bay of Biscay, in the Mediterranean and Black Seas, and also particularly off the coast of West Africa. Spain and Portugal together land *c.* 150,000 tons annually, Angola and South Africa *c.* 300,000 tons.

They are prepared in the same way as sardines, and are marketed either fresh or smoked. They are also used in the preparation of fish meal.

There are related species in all tropical and temperate seas.

79. BASS

Dicentrarchus labrax (L.)

A member of the sea perch and grouper family. The two dorsal fins are the same length and there is a large, black marking on the gill cover. Maximum length *c.* 80 cm (5–7 kg).

A very voracious predatory fish, which usually lives in small shoals close to rocky coasts and in large estuaries. The main area of distribution lies to the south of the British Isles. Spawning takes place in May-August, the female laying pelagic eggs. Feeds on small herring and other shoaling fishes. Bass are caught in the Bay of Biscay, off Portugal and in the Mediterranean, in traps and on various hook and line equipment.

33 cm

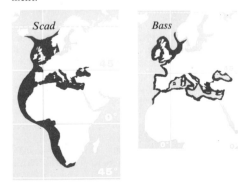
Scad   Bass

80. Ray's bream

Brama brama (Bonnaterre)

Maximum length *c.* 70 cm (*c.* 6 kg). Lives pelagically in depths of 100 m and below, but its biology is completely unknown. It is taken in small numbers in the Mediterranean as an incidental catch of the long line fishery. In autumn a few individuals reach as far as southern Norway and the Skagerrak.

The closely related species *Pterycombus brama* is distinguished by the fact that the dorsal and anal fins can be laid down in longitudinal grooves formed by large scales along the fin bases. It is also a pelagic, deep-sea fish which is widely distributed in the eastern Atlantic.

81. Meagre

Argyrosomus regium (Asso)

Belongs to the drum family (Sciaenidae) which is very close to the sea perch.
Characteristics: second dorsal fin twice as long as the first. Anal fin short. Maximum length *c.* 1·5 m.

Pelagic·predators that move around in small shoals, feeding mainly on other fishes. Rarely recorded north of the English Channel. Taken as an incidental catch off Portugal, in the Bay of Biscay and in the Mediterranean.

The drum family has a worldwide distribution and numerous species. With the help of the swimbladder they can make loud drumming or scratching noises. These noises can even be heard from depths of several metres.

82. Red mullet

Mullus surmuletus L.

Rarely over 40 cm; longevity *c.* 10 years. From the southern and main part of their range some red mullets penetrate to the Channel coasts where they spawn in July-September. The eggs are pelagic and are sometimes swept far north by the currents, and in certain years the young are found along the coasts of the North Sea. Sexually mature at an age of 2 years.

Red mullet live on sandy or rocky bottoms and feed on small bottom-living animals, which the sensitive barbels help them to find. They were famous in ancient times on account of their brilliant changes of colour and their tasty flesh. The total catch in southern Europe, including the Black Sea, is *c.* 7,000 tons.

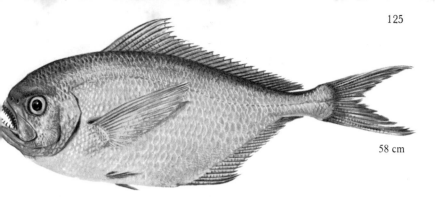

58 cm

80. RAY'S BREAM

Brama brama

120 cm

81. MEAGRE

Argyrosomus regium

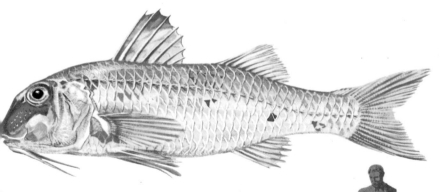

82. RED MULLET

Mullus surmuletus

56 cm

Insult not your gold-inlaid dishes with a small mullet; it ought
to weigh at least two pounds.

MARTIAL (40–104 A.D.)

126

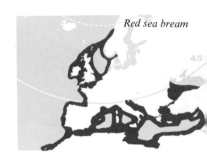

37 cm

83. RED SEA BREAM

Pagellus bogaraveo

SEA BREAM

Body usually tall and laterally compressed. Front half of the dorsal fin with spiny rays, rear half with jointed rays. The anal fin and the jointed-ray part of the dorsal fin are the same length. Teeth pointed, chisel-like or rounded, according to the diet.

The sea bream family contains *c.* 200 species which occur in all warm and temperate coastal waters. Several species are vegetarian.

83. Red sea bream

Pagellus bogaraveo (Brünnich)

Characteristics: a black spot above the pectoral fin at the start of the lateral line. Dorsal fin with 12 spiny rays and 13 jointed rays, anal fin with 3 spiny and 12 jointed rays.

Maximum length 50 cm, longevity *c.* 15 years. Lives mainly in depths of 200–500 m, and feed on crustaceans and pteropods. Spawns in winter. Caught mainly off Britain, France, Spain and Portugal. The total annual catch in Europe is over 10,000 tons, but this fluctuates considerably from year to year.

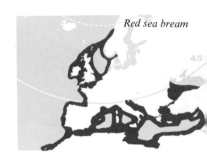

Red sea bream

84. Pandora

Pagellus erythrinus (L.)

Characteristics: without a black spot above the pectoral fin. Dorsal fin with 12 spiny and 10 jointed rays, anal fin with 3 spiny and 8–10 jointed rays.

Maximum length *c.* 50 cm. A visitor to the southern coast of England, but rare in the North Sea. Of some economic importance in the Mediterranean.

34 cm

84. PANDORA

Pagellus erythrinus

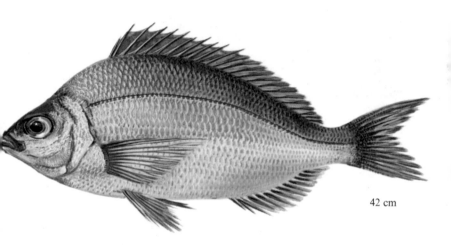

42 cm

35. BLACK SEA BREAM

Spondyliosoma cantharus (L.)

Characteristics: without a black spot above the pectoral fin. Dorsal fin with 11 spiny and 13 jointed rays, anal fin with 3 spiny and 11 jointed rays.

Maximum length *c.* 50 cm. Not common in the North Sea. Of no economic importance.

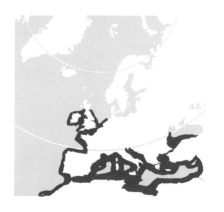

WRASSE

Dorsal fin with a spiny and a jointed ra[
part. Lips thick, jaws with strong teeth
Brightly coloured fishes of the algal zone
especially on rocky coasts.

Identification key

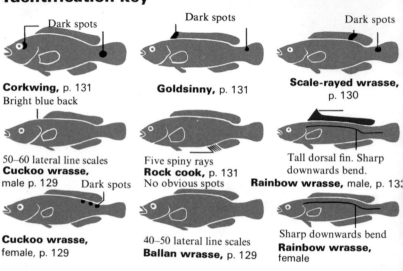

Corkwing, p. 131
Bright blue back

Goldsinny, p. 131

Scale-rayed wrasse,
p. 130

50–60 lateral line scales
Cuckoo wrasse,
male p. 129

Five spiny rays
Rock cook, p. 131
No obvious spots

Tall dorsal fin. Sharp
downwards bend.
Rainbow wrasse, male, p. 13[

Cuckoo wrasse,
female, p. 129

40–50 lateral line scales
Ballan wrasse, p. 129

Sharp downwards bend
Rainbow wrasse,
female

---

86. Cuckoo wrasse

Labrus mixtus L.

Coloration strikingly different in the two
sexes, and often very variable. Females
with 2–3 dark spots on the back and caudal
peduncle. Old males with characteristic
pattern of blue-black stripes; young males
similar in colour to the females, but without the dorsal spots.

Length: males 35 cm, females 30 cm.
Lives in the algal zone on rocky coasts,
and feeds on molluscs and crustaceans.
Spawns on the bottom in summer. Of no
economic value.

87. Ballan wrasse

Labrus berggyylta (Ascanius)

Distinctive features: see identification key
Scales large, usually with a yellow-green
or brown border. Coloration very variable,
greenish and brownish tones predominat-
ing. No external differences between the
sexes.

Rarely over 30 cm, maximum length
50 cm. Lives in the algal zone on rocky
coasts in depths of 5–30 m. The eggs are
laid on the bottom in summer. Feeds on
molluscs and crustaceans. Of no great
economic importance.

male, 33 cm

female, 26 cm

86. CUCKOO WRASSE
Labrus mixtus

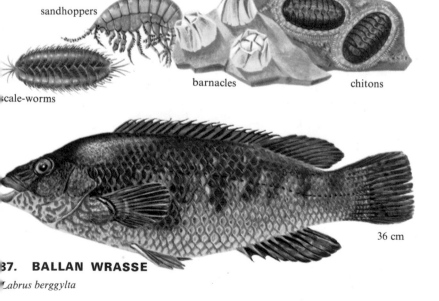

sandhoppers

barnacles

chitons

scale-worms

36 cm

87. BALLAN WRASSE
Labrus berggylta

130

88. Corkwing

Crenilabrus melops (L.)

Distinctive features: See key, p. 128.

Maximum length 25 cm. Coloration very variable; the ground colour of the males is greenish or blue, of the females brownish to yellowish. Lives in the algal zone, usually on rocky coasts, and spawns in summer. Males and females ready to spawn have well-developed genital papillae. The sticky eggs are laid on pieces of seaweed. Feeds on small crustaceans and molluscs.

Of no economic importance.

89. Goldsinny

Ctenolabrus rupestris (L.)

Easily distinguished by the black spot on the upper part of the caudal peduncle and a second one at the front end of the dorsal fin.

Becomes sexually mature at the end of the second year when 15–18 cm long. Widely distributed in the seaweed zone in depths of 0–20 m. Spawns in the summer months; the transparent eggs (diameter 1 mm) and young are pelagic. The parent fish probably die after spawning. Feed on small crustaceans and worms. Of no economic importance.

Goldsinny

90. Rock cook

Centrolabrus exoletus (L.)

Distinctive features: Anal fin with 5 spin rays. No black spots on the body.

Maximum length 18 cm. Lives in th seaweed zone, but is not so widely distri buted as the goldsinny. The eggs are lai during the summer on seaweeds.

The scale-rayed wrasse, *Acantholabru palloni*, is a less common, more southerl species with a slender body and a blac

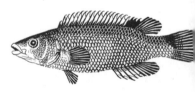

spot at the junction between the spiny an jointed parts of the dorsal fin. There i usually a second black spot on the uppe part of the caudal peduncle.

Rock cook

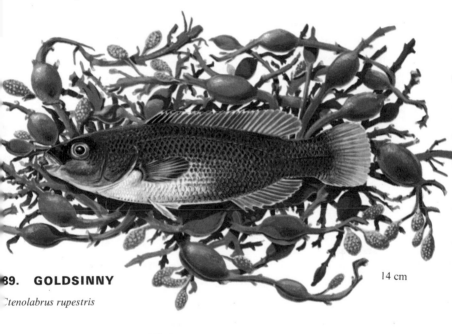

17 cm

88. CORKWING

Crenilabrus melops

89. GOLDSINNY

Ctenolabrus rupestris

14 cm

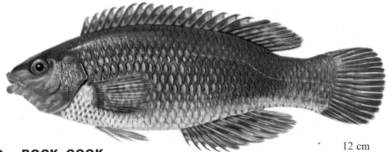

0. ROCK COOK   *Centrolabrus exoletus*

12 cm

91. Rainbow wrasse

Coris julis (L.)

Dorsal fin with less than 13 spiny rays. In males the first dorsal fin rays are considerably longer than those behind. Coloration very variable.

Up to 25 cm long. A rare visitor north of the English Channel. Lives on rocky coasts. Spawns in the summer months, the eggs and young being pelagic. Feeds on small crustaceans and molluscs.

Rainbow wrasse

92. Greater sand-eel

Hyperoplus lanceolatus (Lesauvage)

Distinctive features: The tips of the pectoral fins only just reach as far as the front of the dorsal fin. A dark spot on either side of the snout. Mouth very protrusible (fig. 92).

Average length 20 cm, maximum length 35 cm. In summer this species lives in shallower water than in winter. Habits similar to those of the sand-eel (no. 93). In the North Sea spawning takes place in April-August in depths of *c.* 20 m. The eggs hatch in 2-3 weeks.

Caught together with the sand-eel.

93. Sand-eel

Ammodytes tobianus L.

Distinctive features: The tips of the pectoral fins reach behind the front end of the dorsal fin. Without a dark spot on either side of the snout. Mouth very protrusible (fig. 93).

Reaches a length of *c.* 16 cm at the end of the 3rd year, maximum length 20 cm, longevity 4 years. Lives on sandy bottoms in depths of 0–30 m. Often spends the day buried in the sand, but is active at night when it moves around in small shoals.

This species has 60–66 vertebrae, spawns from August to October and occurs northwards to Iceland and the Faeroes. The related *A. marinus* has 66–72 vertebrae; it spawns in January to March and is widely

distributed from the Murmansk coast to the North Sea, and also off Iceland.

At spawning time the female lays 3,800–22,000 oval eggs (diameter 0·7–1 mm) in small piles on sandy ground. The pelagic larvae are 4–8 mm long on hatching.

Sand-eels feed on animal plankton, worms, crustaceans and small fish. They themselves form an important part of the food of cod, salmon, and other economically valuable fish.

Sand-eels are caught in fine-mesh trawl (mainly in the North Sea) and are processed. Denmark 100,000–400,000 tons, Germany 5,000–20,000 tons. At low tide sand-eels can be dug out of the sand as it dries out. They are eaten and used as bait.

94. Smooth Sand-eel

Gymnammodytes semisquamatus (Jourdain)

Distinctive features: Dorsal fin with a wavy edge. Usually with dark markings on the

Greater sand-eel and Sand-eel

22 cm

91. RAINBOW WRASSE

Coris julis

23 cm

92. GREATER SAND-EEL

Hyperoplus lanceolatus

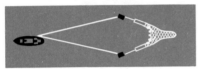

Sand-eels are caught in fine-mesh trawls. They feed on zooplankton and are eaten by many commercially valuable fishes.

93. SAND-EEL

Ammodytes tobianus

14 cm

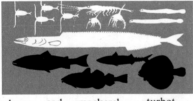

salmon   cod   mackerel   turbot

12 cm

94. SMOOTH SAND-EEL

head. Front part of the body without scales.

Length 15 cm. Lives mainly on shell gravel (a mixture of small stones and mollusc shells). Spawns in the summer months in the North Sea. There is a separate species *G. cicerellus* in the Mediterranean.

95. Greater weever

Trachinus draco L.

The spiny rays of the first dorsal fin and the powerful spine on each gill cover have deep grooves containing venom gland tissue. These can cause extremely painful wounds and inflammation. The venom attacks the blood corpuscles, so any wounds should be allowed to bleed freely.

This species is distinguished from the next by having 2–3 small spines at the front, upper edge of the orbit.

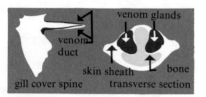

Average length 20–30 cm, maximum length 42 cm. Lives during the summer months in depths of 5–15 m, usually spending the day buried up to the eyes in loose sand, waiting for prey. At night it swims around freely and often small shoals are caught in fixed nets. Migrates into deeper water in the autumn. Feeds on prawns, gobies, dragonets etc.

Spawning takes place in June-August, and the pelagic eggs are *c.* 1 mm in diameter.

Mainly taken as an incidental catch in nets and on hooks. On account of the danger, the head and first dorsal fin ar removed before the fish are marketed. Th dry but tasty flesh is especially esteeme in southern Europe. There are no statisti for the amounts caught in different cou tries.

96. Lesser weever

Trachinus vipera Cuvier

Distinctive features: Without spines at th upper edge of the orbit. Body height les than 5 times the total length.

Length 10–15 cm. In contrast to th preceding species, it lives the whole tim in shallow, sandy coastal areas, onl moving into somewhat deeper water a spawning time (June-August). Feeds o prawns, young fish, small bottom inverte brates and fish spawn.

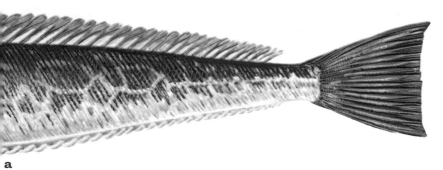

a

95. GREATER WEEVER

Trachinus draco

a 32 cm
b principal food
c principal fishing methods

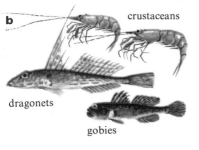

crustaceans

dragonets

gobies

c hook and line

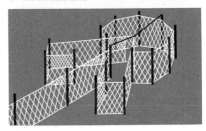

fixed net

11 cm

96. LESSER WEEVER

Trachinus vipera

97. Dragonet

Callionymus lyra L.

Brightly coloured, bottom-living fish with a broad head, eyes directed obliquely upwards and a small mouth with a pro-

trusible upper jaw. Gill opening reduced to a small hole. Skin slimy and scaleless. Sexes very different, the males being somewhat larger than the females.

Males up to 30 cm long, females up to 25 cm. Live on sandy bottoms, from shallow water down to depths of 400 m (or more).

Snout length $1\frac{1}{2}$–2 times the diameter of the eye (cf. spotted dragonet).

Spawns in January-August, the eggs being laid in depths of 20–40 m. The males perform a 'nuptial dance' in front of the females. During spawning the two fish rise slowly towards the surface, with their bodies held close together. The eggs and larvae are pelagic. The young fish do not move down to the bottom until they are *c.* 10 mm long.

Dragonets feed on small crustaceans and molluscs. They are often caught in trawls, and are processed into fish meal.

98. Spotted dragonet

Callionymus maculatus Rafinesque-Schmaltz

Distinctive features: Snout short, as long as the eye diameter. First dorsal fin of the male only slightly taller than the second.

Males up to 16 cm long, females up to 13 cm. Habits similar to those of the dragonet. They appear to be relatively uncommon on the French coast and in the southern North Sea, but are frequently caught in the Kattegat.

Of no importance to the fisheries, any that are caught in trawls being processed into fish meal.

99. Sand-smelt

Atherina presbyter Valenciennes

Sand-smelts are small, shoaling fishes related to grey mullet. They live close to the coast over sandy bottoms, and often enter estuaries. Some species occur only in fresh water.

The present species occurs from the Mediterranean Sea to the coasts of Holland. Occasional shoals have been seen in the Kattegat and the Danish Belt. Length 12–15 cm. Feeds on small crustaceans. Spawning takes place in April-July and the eggs adhere to seaweed.

Caught in seines and other nets and of some slight economic importance in the Mediterranean.

Dragonet   Spotted dragonet   Sand-smelt

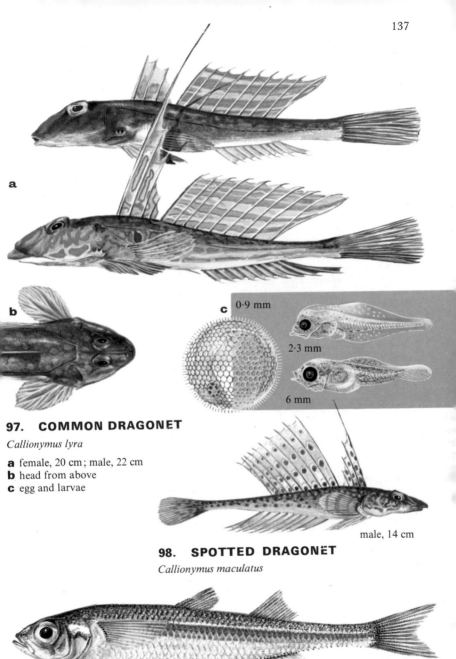

97. COMMON DRAGONET

Callionymus lyra

a female, 20 cm; male, 22 cm
b head from above
c egg and larvae

0·9 mm
2·3 mm
6 mm

male, 14 cm

98. SPOTTED DRAGONET

Callionymus maculatus

15 cm

99. SAND-SMELT

Atherina presbyter

GREY MULLET

With two short dorsal fins, the first composed of four spiny rays. Mouth small. The teeth are small or absent. Scales large, but no lateral line. Wide gill opening and a fine gill filter.

The family contains *c.* 100 species in tropical and temperate seas. They are active, shoaling fishes which mostly live in shallow water above a soft bottom and in dense vegetation; often in lagoons and estuaries.

They feed on planktonic organisms, snails and other invertebrates living among the seaweed, and on plant material. As an adaptation to this type of diet, grey mullet have a very muscular stomach and a strikingly long intestine.

In many places they are of great importance to the fisheries, e.g. in the Black Sea and Caspian Seas. The total annual catch in the Mediterranean (mainly thick-lipped mullet) is *c.* 12,000–16,000 tons. They are caught in fixed traps and purse seines.

100. Thick-lipped mullet

Crenimugil labrosus (Risso)

Characteristics: upper lip thick and much swollen.

Length up to *c.* 60 cm (4–5 kg). Spawns in spring.

Sometimes migrates in small shoals from its southern area of distribution to the Faeroes and the coasts of Iceland and Scandinavia.

101. Thin-lipped mullet

Liza ramada (Risso)

Characteristics: Upper lip thin, without warts. Ventral fins about four-fifths the length of the pectorals.

Length up to *c.* 70 cm. Spawns in spring. Occasionally recorded off the coasts of Scandinavia.

102. Golden mullet

Liza auratus (Risso)

Characteristics: Upper lip thin, without warts. Ventral fins about two-thirds the length of the pectorals. Head and front of body with a golden sheen. Gill cover with a golden-yellow marking. Length up to *c.* 50 cm. A rare visitor north of the British Isles.

101. THIN-LIPPED MULLET
Liza ramada

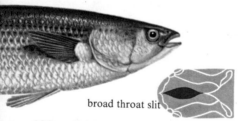

broad throat slit

102. GOLDEN MULLET
Liza auratus

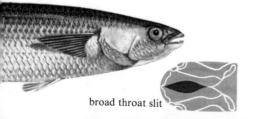

broad throat slit

Thick-lipped mullet, Thin-lipped mullet and Golden mullet

Golden mullet also occur in South African waters

26 cm

narrow throat slit

100. THICK-LIPPED MULLET
Crenimugil labrosus

MACKEREL FAMILY

pelagic, shoaling fishes with spindle-shaped bodies. There are 4–9 separate small fins behind the second dorsal and the anal fin. Inhabitants of tropical and temperate waters, many of which undertake extensive migrations. Some species move northwards in warm years.

These fishes are of great economic importance to world fisheries. The total annual yield is about 2 million tons, of which half is taken by Japan.

Identification key

Dorsal fins widely separated **2**

Dorsal fins close together **4**

With 7–9 finlets .... **Frigate mackerel,** p. 148
With 4–6 finlets **3**

With distinct rows of dots below lateral line .... **Spanish mackerel,** p. 142
Without such dots .... **Mackerel,** p. 140

Pectoral fins long and sickle-shaped, reaching to
behind 2nd dorsal fin .... **Long-fin tunny,** p. 145
Pectorals not reaching beyond 1st dorsal fin **5**

With 4–7 dark, longitudinal stripes below lateral
line .... **Oceanic bonito,** p. 146
With *c.* 7 dark dorsal stripes .... **Pelamid,** p. 147
With 3–5 spots below pectoral fin; dark, irregular
stripes on back .... **False albacore,** p. 145
Without spots or stripes **6**

Front end of dorsal fin tall and pointed, pectorals
reaching beyond the middle of the 1st dorsal fin .... **Tunny,** p. 143

Front end of dorsal fin low, pectorals reaching
only to the middle of 1st dorsal fin .... **Plain bonito,** p. 147

103. MACKEREL

Scomber scombrus L.

a 48 cm
b larva, 14 mm
c principal food
d utilisation
e principal fishing methods

Sexually ripe at the end of the 3rd year when *c*. 30 cm long; maximum length 50 cm. Pelagic, active swimming migratory fishes which often live in shoals close to the surface. They overwinter (at least most do) near the bottom in the northern North Sea and Skagerrak, and also to the south and west of the British Isles, and do not feed during the winter resting period. They start to feed again in the spring mainly on animal plankton (pteropods, small crustaceans) which is sieved from the water taken into the mouth by the gill filter. At the same time they move into the warmer, upper water layers and by April-May they are mostly in coastal waters with a temperature of *c*. 11–14°C. Spawning takes place in May-June off southern England, northern France and in the North Sea, in June-July in the eastern Skagerrak and Kattegat, and in March-April in the Mediterranean. They spawn near the surface, the female producing 200,000–450,000 pelagic eggs, which have a diameter of 0·9–1·4 mm. These hatch in about 6 days into larvae that are 3·5–4·5 mm long. The young fish do not leave the coast until autumn; after 2 years they have reached a length of 20 cm.

After spawning the adult mackerel start to feed very actively, moving about in

small shoals, hunting for small herring, sprats and sand-eels, until they leave the coastal waters again in August-September. Mackerel do not have a swimbladder and so, when chased by their enemies (spur-dogs, porbeagles, tunny, dolphins) they can reach very considerable depths or rise to the surface.

Mackerel are caught in drift nets, seines, beach seines, fixed nets and on hook and line. They are marketed smoked or fresh

(for export, usually deep-frozen), and are also canned.

The total European catch is 600,000–800,000 tons, of which Norway and the Soviet Union take c. 200,000 tons each, Poland 100,000 tons, France 30,000–45,000 tons, Portugal 20,000–40,000 tons, Denmark 10,000–20,000 tons, Italy 5,000–12,000 tons, Holland 7,000–10,000 tons, Britain 4,000–7,000 tons, Sweden 3,000 tons.

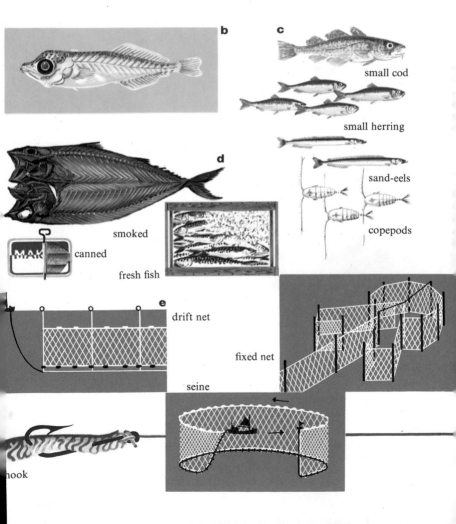

b

c

small cod

small herring

sand-eels

copepods

d

smoked

canned

fresh fish

e drift net

fixed net

seine

hook

30 cm

104. SPANISH MACKEREL

Scomber colias Gmelin

The scales on the breast and the eyes are larger than in the mackerel. With grey-blue markings below the lateral line.

Seldom over 32 cm in length (2 kg). Habits and distribution similar to those of the mackerel, but more subtropical and also less numerous. Seldom seen north of the English Channel. Caught in various nets and by a long line. Portugal, Morocco, Greece, Yugoslavia and Turkey each 100–900 tons.

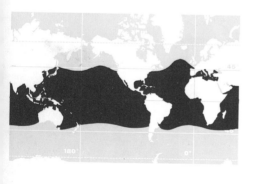

105. Tunny

Thunnus thynnus (L.)

Sexually mature at the end of the 3rd to 4th year when 100–120 cm long (16–27 kg). Rarely over 260 cm in length and 300 kg in weight. Longevity *c.* 15 years. Pelagic migratory fishes which usually live in small shoals close to the surface, preferring temperatures above 10°C. At spawning time (June) they migrate from the Atlantic to the coasts of the Mediterranean. The eggs have a diameter of 1–1·2 mm, but the number produced is not known. They hatch after 2 days into pelagic larvae (4 mm long). The very fast-growing young fish (1–3 years old) move in summer into the waters south of Britain. After spawning the emaciated adults undertake extensive migrations in search of food (up to Norway). By August-September they are leaving northern Europe and probably go to the waters around the Azores.

Tunny feed on shoaling fishes of the open ocean. By means of their gill filters they sieve the larvae of pilchard, anchovy and herring from the water as they quietly swim through the shoals. On the other hand, mackerel, garfish and herring are often attacked by several tunny at the same time, which lash about wildly, killing or stunning their prey. At greater depths they catch redfish and ling.

Tunny are caught in seines, set and anchored traps, gill nets, pelagic long lines and so on. In southern Europe they are mainly caught in anchored pound-nets (Tonnara).

Spain takes 3,000 tons in the Straits of Gibraltar, Italy 4,000 tons, France 3,000 tons, Norway, Morocco, and Portugal 1,000 tons each.

05. TUNNY

Thunnus thynnus

a *c.* 2·50 m
b vertebra, 6 years old
c musculature, transverse section
d principal food
e utilisation
f principal fishing method

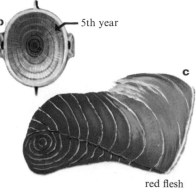

5th year

c

red flesh

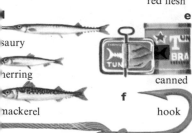

saury

herring

mackerel

e

canned

f

hook

Tunny are highly esteemed on account of their red, fatty flesh. Most of the catch is canned.

There are also several races (or species) off the western coasts of America, and off Japan and Australia.

144

106. False albacore

Euthynnus alletteratus (Rafinesque-Schmaltz)

Characteristics: Irregular dark stripes on the back. A few dark spots below the pectoral fins.

Maximum length 90 cm (*c.* 15 kg). Lives near the coasts. Mainly caught off western Africa; not common in the Bay of Biscay, rare north of the English Channel.

hooks towed by fast boats. Maize leaves o coloured ribbons are used as artificia baits. They are also caught on doub hooks. The head and entrails of tunny ar removed on board.

In Europe, about 10,000 tons are lande

107. Long-fin tunny

Thunnus alalunga (Bonnaterre)

Characteristics: The long pectoral fins reach to behind the second dorsal fin. Individuals 4 years old are 60–70 cm long (*c.* 4 kg); maximum length 110 cm (30 kg). Pelagic fishes living in depths of 0–50 m, and spawning in May-June. Number of eggs produced not known, but estimated at 3–4 millions. After spawning they migrate to higher latitudes in search of food, arriving in the region between Cape Finistère and Ireland during the course of July (*c.* 1 month later than tunny). They prefer waters with a temperature above 15°C and a salinity of 35·5 parts per thousand.

Long-fin tunny feed on small shoaling fishes, euphausians and other large plank-tonic crustaceans and also on squids.

In the Bay of Biscay they are caught on

in France, 25,000 tons in Spain. This is a important commercial fish in Japan (85,000 tons) and the U.S.A. (*c.* 18,0 tons). More than half the catch is canne

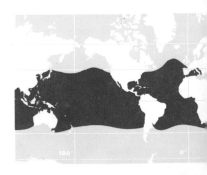

64 cm

◀06. FALSE ALBACORE

Euthynnus alletteratus

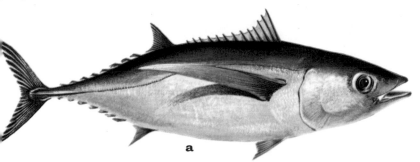

a

107. LONG-FIN TUNNY

Thunnus alalunga

a 60 cm
b principal food
c utilisation
d principal fishing method

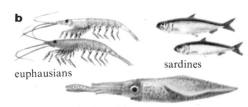

b

euphausians

sardines

pelagic squids

c

canned

d

hook

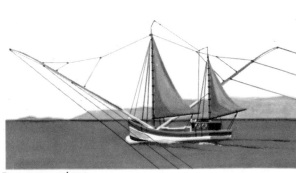

Breton tunny boat

108. OCEANIC BONITO

Katsuwonus pelamis (L.)

Characteristics: With 4–7 dark longitudinal stripes on the belly. Up to 70 cm
long (5 kg). Swims long distances in the
surface waters. Not particularly common,
even in the warmer parts of the Atlantic.
Visits south-western Europe and the Mediterranean during the summer, but rarely
further north than 48°N. Caught in small
numbers together with the long-fin tunny.
It is, however, very abundant in the Pacific
Ocean where it is the most important
commercial species in the tunny group
(up to 45% of the total world catch). Of
particular economic importance to Japan,
U.S.A. and Peru.

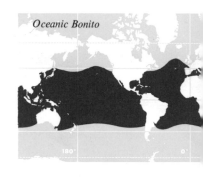

Oceanic Bonito

in the Black Sea and off Morocco, or
hook and line, pelagic long lines and i
seines and drift nets.

The catches are: U.S.S.R. 200–8,00
tons, Turkey 6,000–20,000 tons, also i
smaller numbers in Morocco, Spain an
Portugal. Pelamids are mostly marketed a
fresh fish. There are other importan
related species in the Pacific Ocean.

109. Pelamid

Sarda sarda (Bloch)

Characteristics: With 7–20 oblique longitudinal stripes on the back. Specimens
4 years old are *c.* 70 cm long (5 kg), but
on average less (1–4 kg). Shoaling predators which hunt near the surface for
pilchards, scad and grey mullets. The main
area of distribution is west of Gibraltar
and in the eastern Mediterranean.

Spawns in June, the female laying
420,000 pelagic eggs. After spawning the
shoals break up into small groups which
move long distances in search of food. A
very frequent visitor to the North Sea.

Caught during the spawning migrations

65 cm

109. PELAMID

Sarda sarda

61 cm

110. PLAIN BONITO

Orcynopsis unicolor (St. Hilaire)

Characteristics: Front end of the 1st dorsal fin low, without a point. Body without stripes or spots. Reaching a length of 70 cm (*c.* 3 kg).

In contrast to the other members of the tunny group, this species evidently lives at greater depths. Rare to the north of the English Channel. General habits unknown. Taken as an incidental catch off Morocco.

42 cm

111. FRIGATE MACKEREL

Auxis thazard (Lacépède)

Characteristics: The two dorsal fins are widely separated. Maximum length 50–60 cm. In August-September, small shoals move northwards into the Bay of Biscay, where they are caught together with mackerel and tunny. Rare in the North Sea.

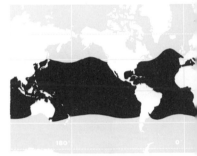

112. SWORDFISH

Xiphias gladius L.

Average length 2–3·5 m (60–150 kg), maximum length *c.* 4·5 m. In adults the 'sword' reaches about a third of the total length.

Open ocean fishes which undertake extensive migrations. Usually live close below the surface, but when chasing shoals of deep-sea fish may reach depths of 500–800 m. Optimum temperature for spawning: 23–24°C. Spawns in the southern part of the Sargasso Sea (February-April) and to a lesser extent in the Mediterranean (June-August). The pelagic eggs have a diameter of 1·6–1·8 mm. The newly hatched young live pelagically in the upper water layers where they quickly develop into very voracious predators. After spawning, the adults remain for a time near the coast where they hunt for mackerel, garfish and herring. When catching prey they lash out wildly with the sword.

Swordfish are caught by harpoon, or on hook and line, and are very popular game fish. They often do considerable damage to fisheries by tearing the nets.

The total European catch is somewhat over 3,000 tons per year, of which *c.* 1,000 tons are landed in Spain. Small specimens are marketed fresh in southern Europe. Some of the catch is canned.

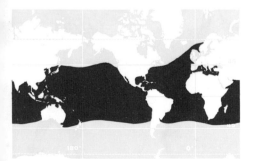

112. SWORDFISH

Xiphias gladius

a *c.* 3 m
b larva, 16 mm
c principal food
d principal fishing method

b

c

saury

flyingfishes

squids

hook

d

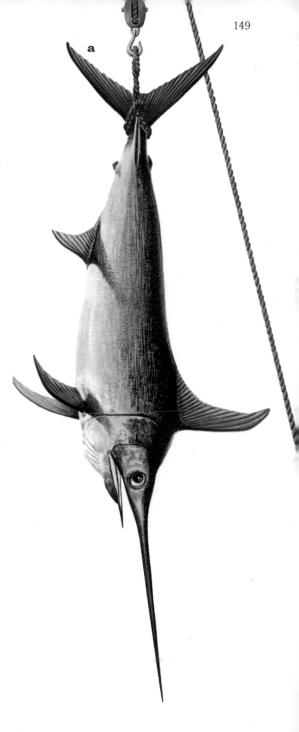

113. Yarrell's blenny

Chirolophis ascanii (Walbaum)

Characteristics: Two pairs of black or reddish-yellow tentacles above the eyes. The tips of the 1st dorsal fin spines also have tentacles, particularly in old males.

Seldom over 15 cm long. Lives in the seaweed zone in depths of 10–20 m, mainly over stony or rocky ground. Spawns in October-November, the eggs being laid on the bottom. The larvae are pelagic. Feeds on small crustaceans and worms. Of no economic importance.

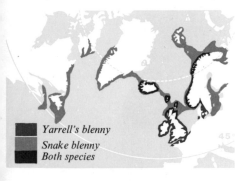

Yarrell's blenny
Snake blenny
Both species

114. Snake blenny

Lumpenus lampretaeformis (Walbaum)

Sexually mature in the 3rd year, when 17–24 cm long. Maximum length 42 cm. Lives on soft bottoms in depths of 50–200 m. The Baltic Sea population is probably a relict from the Ice Age. Spawns on the bottom in December-January. The larvae are pelagic. Feeds on small bottom-living invertebrates (worms, crustaceans).

In the related form *Leptoclinus maculatus* the rear edge of the caudal fin is not pointed. This species reaches a length of *c.* 20 cm and has a similar distribution to *Lumpenus lampretaeformis*, but is absent from the Baltic. Both species form an important part of the diet of cod, but are of no direct economic importance except as bait for long lines.

115. Shanny

Blennius pholis L.

Characteristics: Dorsal fin with a dip in the middle. No tentacles on the head. Coloration very variable. Maximum length 18 cm. Lives along rocky coasts in the temperate zone and is often found in rock-pools and among seaweed when the tide is out. The eggs (diameter 1·5 mm) are laid under stones or in rock crevices.

Other species occurring in south-western Europe are the butterfly blenny, *B. ocellaris* (14 cm long and easily recognised by the large black spot on the dorsal fin), Montagu's blenny, *Coryphoblennius galerita* (7 cm, marked with numerous pale blue spots), and the Tompot blenny, *B. gattorugine* (18 cm), in which the dorsal fin is only slightly indented. All three species have branched or fringed tentacles on the head.

116. Butterfish or Gunnel

Pholis gunnellus (L.)

With 9–13 dark spots along the base of the dorsal fin. Sexually mature in its 3rd year when 17–24 cm long. Lives in the seaweed zone in depths of 0–30 m and feeds on small crustaceans and other invertebrates

The eggs are usually laid under stones or in empty bivalve shells, pressed into a clump and guarded by both parents.

Spawning takes place in November-January. The eggs hatch into larvae 9 mm long which live pelagically until they are *c.* 3 cm long.

Of no economic importance.

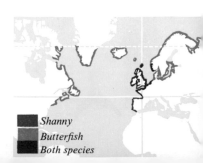

Shanny
Butterfish
Both species

113. YARRELL'S BLENNY *Chirolophis ascanii*

14 cm

114. SNAKE BLENNY
Lumpenus lampretaeformis

33 cm

Leptoclinus maculatus

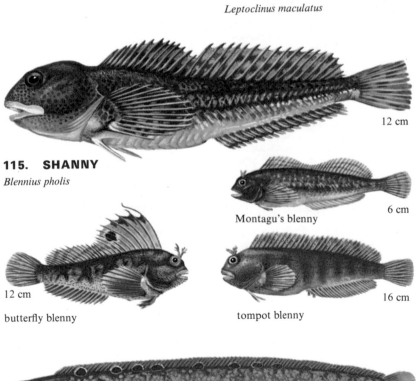

115. SHANNY
Blennius pholis

12 cm

Montagu's blenny

6 cm

butterfly blenny

12 cm

tompot blenny

16 cm

18 cm

116. BUTTERFISH *Pholis gunnellus*

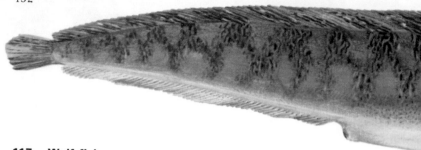

117. Wolf-fish

Anarhichas lupus L.

Sexually mature at the end of the 6th-7th year, when 50–60 cm long (1–3 kg). Maximum length 120 cm. A bottom-living fish which spawns in October-January, the female laying 3,000–24,000 eggs (according to her size). The yellowish eggs (diameter 5–6 mm) are laid in spherical clumps on the sea bottom. After about two months they hatch into pelagic larvae 18 mm long. Wolf-fish feed on hard-shelled bottom-living animals, which they break up with their powerful teeth: crabs, hermit-crabs, sea-urchins, molluscs. Shortly before each spawning season the worn teeth are replaced by new ones growing up from behind.

An important incidental catch in trawls and seines, and some are taken on long lines. Before marketing they are skinned and, because of their frightening appearance, decapitated. They are sold fresh or as smoked or frozen fillets.

The total annual European catch (including spotted catfish) is 25,000–30,000 tons, of which Iceland takes 5,000–8,000 tons, the Soviet Union *c.* 12,000 tons, Britain 4,000–6,000 tons, Germany 2,000–3,000 tons, Norway 2,000 tons.

118. Jelly cat

Lycichthys denticulatus (Krøyer)

Maximum length *c.* 150 cm. Lives on soft bottoms in depths of 300–600 m. General habits and diet similar to those of the wolf-fish. Its flesh is soft and watery, so it is of no value, but it does damage to fisheries by tearing the bait from long lines.

119. Spotted catfish

Anarhichas minor Olafsen

Sexually mature in the 7th–10th year, at a length of 70–90 cm (4–8 kg). Seldom over 140 cm; longevity *c.* 25 years. Lives on the bottom in depths of 100–300 m. In the spring some of them migrate from the eastern Barents Sea to the banks off Finnmark, where they spawn in June-July. A female lays 15,000–35,000 eggs (diameter 5–6 mm).

An important incidental catch, particularly off Norway. Caught in trawls, seine nets and by long line. Marketed fresh or as frozen fillets. A leather is made from the skin of these three species.

a 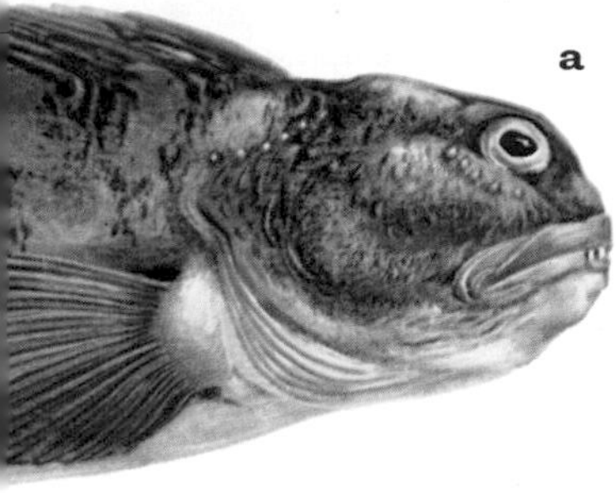
b

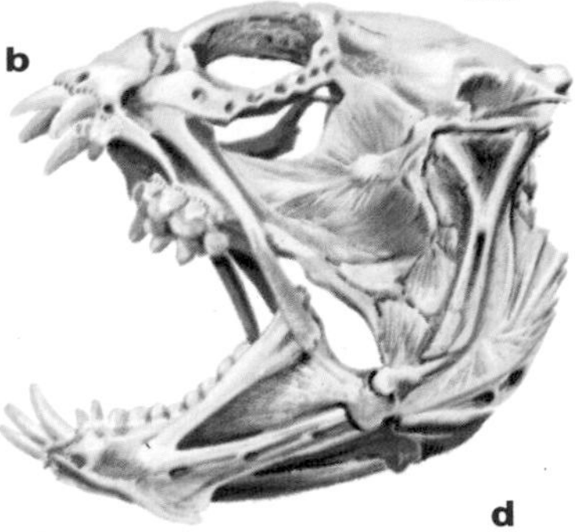

117. WOLF-FISH
Anarhichas lupus

a 51 cm
b skull
c principal food
d principal fishing methods

hermit-crabs

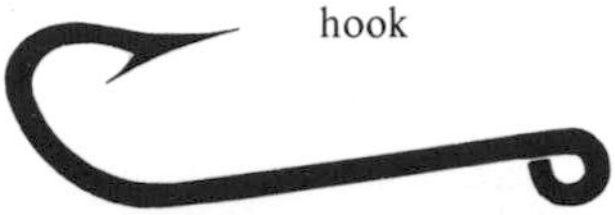

hook

gastropods 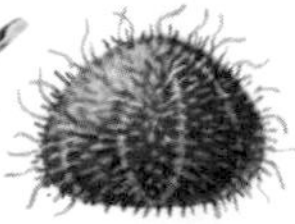   sea-urchins    bivalves 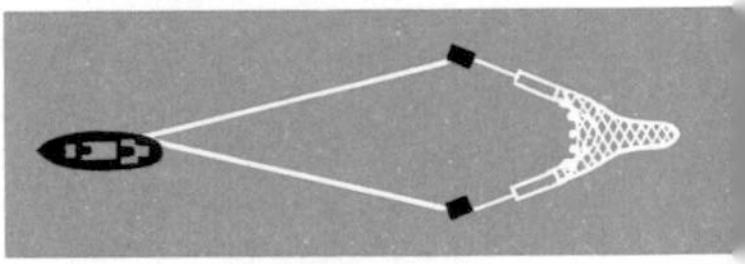   trawl

118. JELLY CAT
Lycicthys denticulatus

100 cm

119. SPOTTED CATFISH
Anarhichas minor

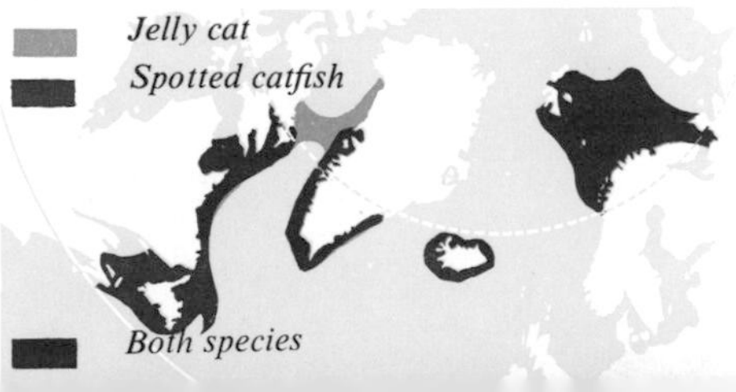

95 cm

Jelly cat
Spotted catfish

Both species

154

120. Eelpout

Zoarces viviparus (L.)

Characteristics: The soft-rayed dorsal fin has at its rear end a short, low section with weak spines. The bones are green, due to a harmless pigment. Skin slimy, with reduced scales. Coloration very variable.

Specimens 3 years old are *c.* 30 cm long. Maximum length 50 cm. A common bottom-living fish in the algal zone, moving into somewhat deeper water in winter. Also abundant in brackish waters. Forms several local races.

The eelpout is viviparous. Mating takes place in August-September, with internal fertilisation of the eggs (diameter 3 mm). After about 4 months the female gives birth to 30–400 fully developed young (length 35–55 mm) which immediately start to live on the bottom. They become sexually mature at the end of their 2nd year, but seldom live for more than 3–4 years. They feed on sandhoppers, worms, molluscs and small fish.

Eelpouts are caught in traps or in fine-mesh seines. They are marketed skinned and fresh, salted or smoked. Some of the catch is used for bait or as food for trout farms.

121. Vahl's eelpout

Lycodes vahli Reinhardt

Characteristics: Dorsal, caudal and anal fins fused. Body eel-shaped. Ventral fins much reduced to two small, short processes on the throat. Front end of the dorsal fin with a few (1–3) blackish-brown spots. Lateral line distinct.

Maximum length off Greenland 40 cm, off Scandinavia rarely over 20 cm. Lives on the bottom in depths of 65–500 m, at temperatures of 0–3°C. Spawns in July-October, the female laying 30–90 eggs on the sea bottom. The eggs (diameter 4·5 mm) hatch into larvae with 8–10 dark transverse bands, which later disappear. Feeds on crustaceans, worms, molluscs.

The genus has several species in the deep, cold parts of northern seas, but these are often very difficult to distinguish from one another. Of no economic importance.

The closely related *Lycenchelys sarsi* (19 cm) occurs along the Norwegian coast in depths of 150–600 m.

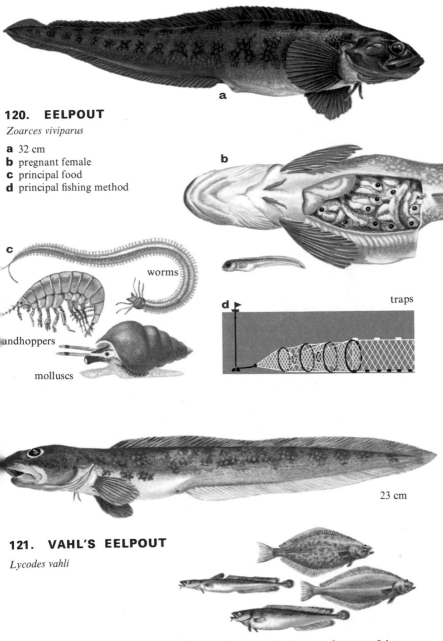

120. **EELPOUT**

Zoarces viviparus

a 32 cm
b pregnant female
c principal food
d principal fishing method

worms

sandhoppers

molluscs

traps

121. **VAHL'S EELPOUT**

Lycodes vahli

23 cm

Vahl's eelpout forms an important food source for many fishes.

GOBIES

Most members of the family Gobiidae are small (5–12 cm long) and live along the coast in shallow water, often in great numbers; there are numerous species throughout the world, and a few occur in fresh water. As food for commercial fishes

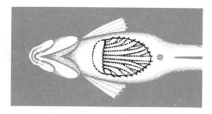

they may have some indirect importance for the fisheries, but they may also be harmful food competitors, e.g. of flatfish fry.

The ventral fins are usually fused to form a flat suction disc. The lateral line is reduced or completely absent, but there are sensory papillae on other parts of the body. The eggs are laid on seaweed, rocks or in empty bivalve shells and are guarded by the male. There are *c.* 10 species in the North Atlantic, of which the largest are sometimes used as bait.

The different species are difficult to distinguish, so only the most important are mentioned here (see also the key, p. 25).

122. Black goby

Gobius niger L.

Specimens 2 years old are *c.* 15 cm long. Maximum length 18 cm. Live among algae, on soft bottoms, in depths of 1–50 m. During May–August the females lay 1,000–6,000 eggs on seaweed, stakes or stones. The male guards the eggs and fans them with water. The pear-shaped eggs (length 0·8 mm) are provided with filaments which enable them to adhere to various objects.

The newly hatched larvae (length 3 mm) are at first pelagic, and do not start to live on the bottom until they are 9 mm long. They are sexually mature at *c.* 1 year and they feed on worms, young fish, sandhoppers and other small crustaceans.

Caught in fine-mesh seine nets and used as bait.

The rock goby, *G. paganellus,* occurs from the English Channel to the Mediterranean. It is similar to the black goby but its dorsal fin has a pale edge and the first four rays are the same length.

Fries's goby, *G. friesi,* occurs from the Skagerrak to the waters around Ireland, in depths of 20–40 m.

Black goby

122. BLACK GOBY

Gobius niger

a male, 15 cm; female, 14 cm
b eggs, 1·5 mm

many fishes feed on gobies.

eggs attached to bladder wrack

123. TWO-SPOT GOBY

Chaparrudo flavescens (Fabricius)

Characteristics: Rear edge of caudal fin straight. A black spot on the middle of the caudal fin base. Males with a second similar spot behind each pectoral fin.

Sexually mature at the end of the 1st year, when *c.* 6 cm long. Longevity rarely over 2 years. Lives in the shallow water of the algal zone, often in large shoals, swimming close beneath the surface. The eggs, which are laid in summer, mostly on plants, are pear-shaped and 1 mm long. They hatch into pelagic larvae 2·5 mm long.

male, 4·8 cm

124. Sand Goby

Gobius minutus (Pallas)

Characteristics: 61–73 scales in a longitudinal row.

Maximum length 11 cm. Sexually mature after 1 year. Lives on the bottom, sometimes in small shoals, in depths of 4–200 m. Spawning takes place in summer when the female lays her eggs usually inside empty bivalve shells. The male guards the spawn for about 9 days, until they hatch into larvae that are 3 mm long. The larvae are at first pelagic and the young fish only start to live on the bottom when they are 17–18 mm long.

125. Painted goby

Pomatoschistus pictus (Malm)

Similar to the sand goby but the two dorsal fins are closer together. On the middle of each flank there are 4–5 brownish markings, which are often double. Both dorsal fins have two longitudinal rows of black spots.

Maximum length 5·5 cm, longevity 1–2 years. Lives on hard bottoms down to depths of 100 m. Spawns in summer, the pear-shaped eggs being *c.* 1 mm in diameter. The newly hatched larvae are 3 mm long and pelagic, and they do not start to live on the bottom until they are 17–18 mm long. They avoid brackish water.

On the other hand, the common goby, *P. microps*, is frequently found in brackish water. It is very similar to the painted goby but has somewhat larger scales, a greenish back and *c.* 8 brownish spots on the middle of each flank. The dorsal fin has indistinct brownish markings. Distributed in brackish water, in depths of 0–12 m. Spawns in summer, the eggs being 1 mm long. The newly hatched larvae are 3 mm long and live pelagically until they are 11–12 mm long.

126. Crystal goby

Crystallogobius linearis (Düben)

Body glassy and translucent. The first dorsal and the ventral fins are much reduced in the female, and in the male the first dorsal has only two rays. At spawning time the male develops two large teeth at the tip of the lower jaw.

Males reach a length of up to 5 cm, females up to 4 cm. Longevity 1 year. Pelagic, shoaling fishes in depths of 1–400 m. The eggs are laid in the empty tubes of tube-worms and guarded by the male.

127. Transparent goby

Aphia minuta (Risso)

Body glassy and translucent. First dorsal fin with 5 spiny rays. Dorsal and anal fins longer in the male than in the female.

Maximum length of the male 6 cm, of the female 5 cm. Longevity 1 year. Lives in shallow water, usually in dense swarms. The eggs are laid in summer in empty bivalve shells.

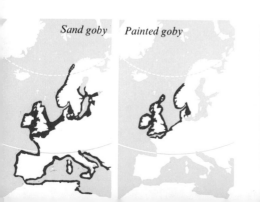

Sand goby   Painted goby

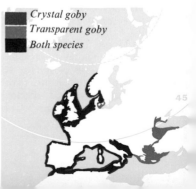

Crystal goby
Transparent goby
Both species

124. SAND GOBY

Gobius minutus

a male, 8 cm
b egg, 1 mm

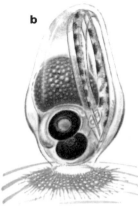

male, 4·5 cm

125. PAINTED GOBY

Pomatoschistus pictus

egg attached to bivalve shell

126. CRYSTAL GOBY

Crystallogobius linearis

a male, 4·5 cm; female, 3·6 cm
b head of male

127. TRANSPARENT GOBY

Aphia minuta

a male, 5·5 cm; female, 4·6 cm
b head of male

160

128. Redfish

Sebastes marinus (L.)

Characteristics: Lateral line with 80–90 scales. Between the rear end of the anal fin and the lateral line there are 16–21 scales (counting diagonally forwards). Mouth pale red. Male with a distinct genital papilla.

Sexually mature at a length of *c*. 38 cm, when in its 11th year. Maximum length 1 m (over 60 years old, 15 kg). Lives close to the coast, near the bottom in depths of 100–400 m and also at lesser depths. Its habits have been little investigated as it is very difficult to bring it to the surface alive. When hauled up from a depth the large expansible swimbladder forces out the eyes and internal organs.

Redfish are viviparous. The main breeding grounds are off the Lofotens, Iceland and Newfoundland. In October-November there are large shoals of redfish in the northern Barents Sea where they mate. Then in the winter months the females move to the steep slopes off the Lofotens and Vesterålen, where in April-July in depths of 200–500 m at a temperature of 4–8·5°C, they give birth to 37,000–350,000 larvae. After this the females migrate and rejoin the shoals of males. The newly born larvae (length 5–7 mm) live in the surface waters and only move down into deeper waters as they grow older. The rate of growth is slow. Redfish feed on pelagic crustaceans, arrow-worms and cod spawn, and the largest ones live mainly on herring and capelin.

The closely related *S. mentella* lives in great depths. It differs from *S. marinus* in having larger eyes and a bony process on the lower jaw.

Redfish are caught by trawl and long line, and to a lesser extent as a by-product of the prawn trawl.

The total annual catch is *c*. 400,000 tons, of which Germany, Canada and the Soviet Union take 100,000 tons each, Iceland 25,000–30,000 tons, U.S.A. 25,000 tons, and Britain 8,000 tons.

It is marketed in the form of deep-

frozen fillets, and some is sold fresh, salt or smoked. The liver yields an oil rich vitamins.

129. Norway haddock

Sebastes viviparus (Krøyer)

Characteristics: Lateral line with 70–8 scales. Between the rear end of the an fin and the lateral line there are only 1 13 scales (counting diagonally forwards Mouth pale red.

Average length 20–30 cm. Coastal an bottom-living fish in depths of 50–300 n In summer the female produces 12,000 30,000 young, 4–5 mm long. The annua growth is very small. Taken as an incident catch in prawn trawls, but of no econom importance.

Its more southerly relative, the blu mouth (*Helicolenus dactylopterus*) occu off Ireland, Scotland and western Norwa This species has a blue mouth and 8 part free rays in each pectoral fin.

28. REDFISH

bastes marinus

51 cm
larva, 12 mm
principal food
utilisation
principal fishing methods

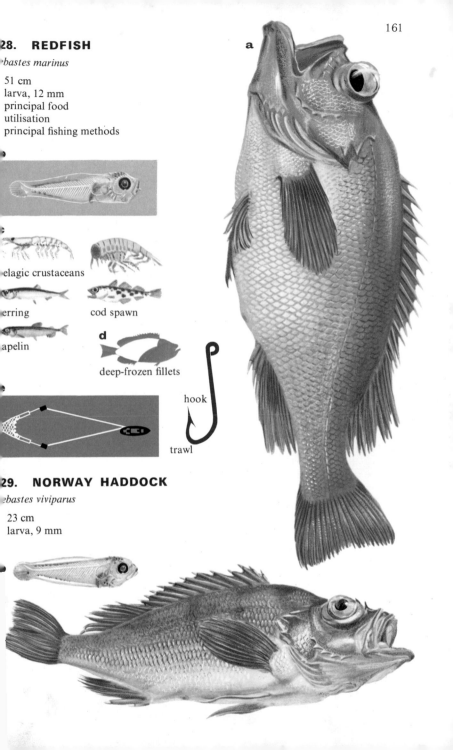

elagic crustaceans

erring   cod spawn

apelin

d

deep-frozen fillets

hook

trawl

29. NORWAY HADDOCK

ebastes viviparus

23 cm
larva, 9 mm

GURNARDS

The head has a strong armour of dermal bones. The three lowermost pectoral fin rays are separated like fingers and can be moved independently; they serve as tactile and locomotory organs. With the help of special muscles, which set the swimbladder vibrating, the gurnards can produce dull, grunting sounds, the function of which is not yet known.

130. Grey gurnard

Eutrigla gurnardus (L.)

Characteristics: The pectoral fins do not reach beyond the start of the anal fin. Lateral line with keeled, bony scutes. Widely distributed.

The males are sexually mature from their 3rd year at a length of *c.* 18 cm, the females in the 4th year when *c.* 24 cm long. Maximum length 45 cm. Bottom-living in depths of 10–150 m, on soft or mixed ground, but also often found free-swimming. Approaches the coasts in summer. Spawns in April-August, the female laying 200,000–300,000 pelagic eggs (diameter *c.* 1·4 mm). These hatch in 8–10 days into larvae which feed on zooplankton. The adults feed on small, bottom-living fishes, prawns and crabs. Caught incidentally by trawl and long line, and eaten in some countries.

Grey gurnard
Red gurnard
Both species

131. Tub gurnard

Trigla lucerna L.

Characteristics: Skin and lateral li smooth.

Average length 25–50 cm, maximu 75 cm. Habits similar to those of tl grey gurnard, but feeds mainly on fishe sprats, pilchards, sand-smelts and fi eggs. An excellent swimmer which som times jumps up far above the surface. A incidental catch in trawl and on long lin Highly esteemed in many countries account of its firm white flesh. Tl European gurnard catch (mostly tub gu nards) amounts to about 8,000 to annually: Spain 4,000–5,000 tons, Brita 1,400 tons.

A more southerly species, the piper (*lyra*). has a very long spine behind t gill cover which extends to half the leng of the pectoral fin. It occurs off southe England in depths of 200 m.

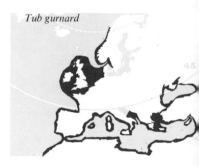

Tub gurnard

132. Red gurnard

Aspitrigla cuculus (L.)

Characteristics: The lateral line has bo extensions which form transverse ridg that extend up to the dorsal fins. Leng 30–40 cm. Habits similar to those of t two preceding species. Caught by tra and long line.

In the more southerly streaked gurna *Trigloporus lastoviza*, the lateral line sca are not elongated; its body has seve oblique transverse bands.

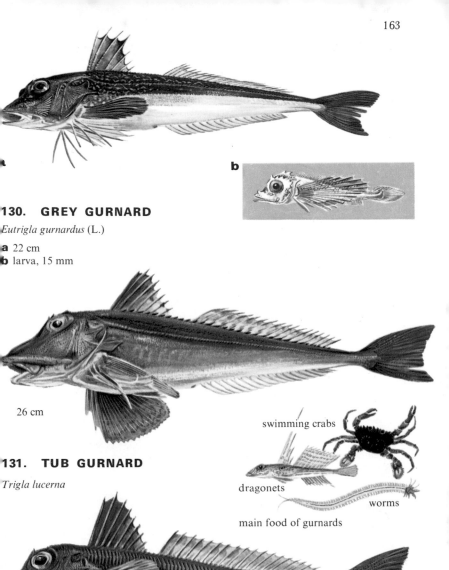

130. GREY GURNARD

Eutrigla gurnardus (L.)

a 22 cm
b larva, 15 mm

26 cm

131. TUB GURNARD

Trigla lucerna

swimming crabs

dragonets

worms

main food of gurnards

20 cm

132. RED GURNARD

Aspitrigla cuculus

COTTIDS

Predatory bottom-living fishes with a large head and no swimbladder. Only found in the northern hemisphere, with a few species in fresh water.

Identification Key

1 {
Body armoured with bony plates .... **Pogge,** p. 167
With bony knobs on lateral line **2**
Without bony knobs on lateral line **4**

2 {
A 2nd row of bony knobs above lateral line **3**
Front gill cover with long, powerful spine .... **Sea scorpion,** p. 167

3 {
Eye diameter equals snout length, anal fin with 20 rays.................................... *Triglops pingeli**
Eye diameter equals snout length, anal fin with 8 rays .... **Norway bullhead,** p. 165

Eye diameter less than snout length, anal fin with 15 rays... *Icelus bicornis**

4 {
Skull with longitudinal keels, head large, broad .... **Father lasher,** p. 165
Skull without longitudinal keel, front gill cover with long, branched spine .... *Gymnocanthus triscuspis**
Skull with 4 large knobs........................ **Four-horned cottus,** p. 167

Skull without longitudinal keel, front gill cover with 2 spines, the upper one hook-like................... *Artediellus uncinatus**

*Species only mentioned in the identification key.

133. Father lasher

Myoxocephalus scorpius (L.)

Characteristics: See identification key. Males sexually mature at a length of 14–25 cm, females at 15–30 cm, at the end of the 2nd year. Maximum length in the Arctic: 60 cm. Lives in the algal zone; there are numerous local forms. At spawning time the male has a deep red belly with white spots, and during pairing he holds the female with the large, rough pectoral and ventral fins. The eggs are laid on the bottom in clumps which are guarded by the male. The eggs, which have a diameter of 2–2·5 mm, hatch in about 5 weeks and the larvae are pelagic until they are about 15 mm long.

The father lasher is a very voracious predator which feeds on crustaceans, and also on the eggs and larvae of commercial fishes, thus causing damage to the fisheries. Used as bait and for the preparation of fish meal, and in Greenland they are also eaten.

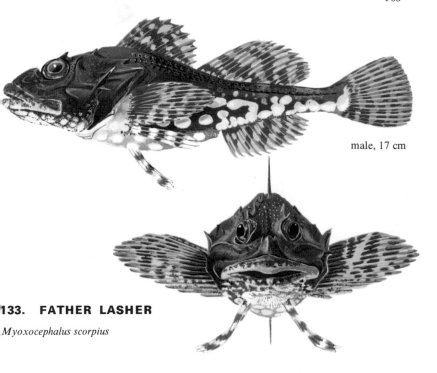

male, 17 cm

133. FATHER LASHER

Myoxocephalus scorpius

5·5 cm

134. NORWAY BULLHEAD

Taurulus lilljeborgi (Collett)

Characteristics: See identification key. Length 5–6 cm. Lives in depths of 25–100 m. The eggs are laid and attached to polyp colonies in April. The larvae are pelagic until July-August. The habits and distribution are not fully known.

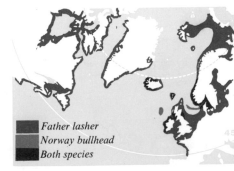

Father lasher
Norway bullhead
Both species

135. Sea scorpion

Taurulus bubalis (Euphrasen)

Characteristics: See identification key. Males sexually mature at a length of 10–15 cm, females at 14–18 cm, at the end of the 2nd year; they seldom become larger. Habits similar to those of the father lasher, but less abundant. Feeds on crustaceans and fish eggs and spawns in February-May.

136. Four-horned cottus

Oncocottus quadricornis (L.)

With four large, greyish-yellow knobs on the head. Maximum length *c.* 30 cm. A northern, bottom-living fish that feeds mainly on crustaceans and worms. During the last Ice Age its distribution extended much further south. When the ice retreated, about 6,000 years ago, many local forms were left behind in fresh waters, because their access to the sea had been cut off These managed to become adapted to th changed conditions, and so the four-horne cottus is found as a relict in the deep cold lakes of North America and Nort Europe. These populations are quite iso ated from one another, and so sever local races or subspecies have been recog nised. The characteristic 'horns' are muc smaller in the freshwater forms than in the marine relatives.

Their habits are similar to those of th preceding species.

137. Pogge

Agonus cataphractus (L.)

Head and body completely covered wit an armour of keeled, bony plates. Wit several short bristles on underside of head

Average length 12–15 cm, maximur 20 cm. A typical demersal fish on so bottoms in depths of 5–200 m. Spawns i February-April, the female laying yello eggs (diameter 1·8–2·2 mm) in small clump between the branched, root-like holdfas of brown seaweeds. The period of develop ment is very long, and the eggs do no hatch for 10–11 months. The larvae ar pelagic until 20 mm long. Pogges feed o prawns and other small crustaceans.

The closely related northern specie *Leptogonus decagonus* has fewer barbel it occurs off Iceland, the Faeroes an northern Norway. Another closely relate species lives off the coasts of Greenland.

10 cm

135. SEA SCORPION

Taurulus bubalis

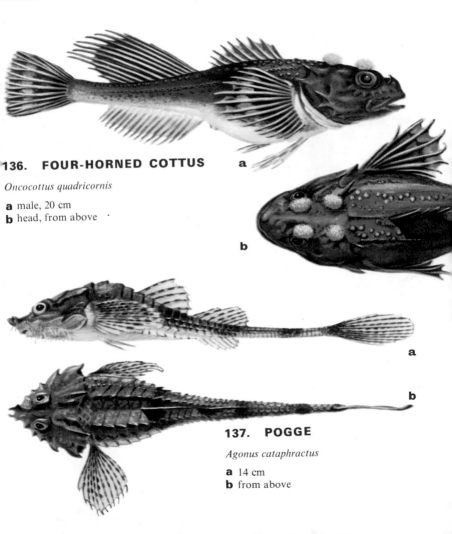

136. FOUR-HORNED COTTUS

a

Oncocottus quadricornis

a male, 20 cm
b head, from above

b

a

b

137. POGGE

Agonus cataphractus

a 14 cm
b from above

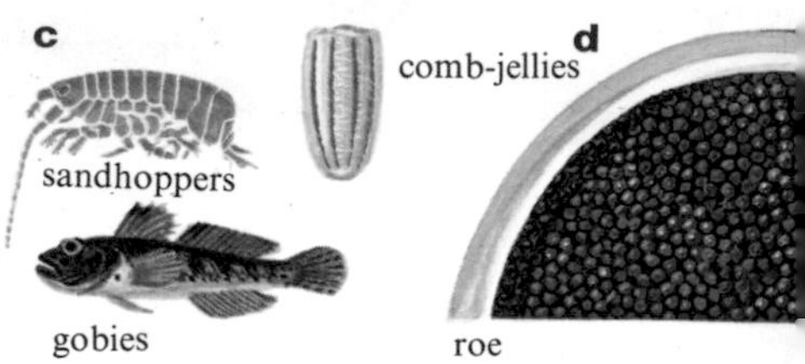

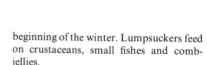

138. LUMPSUCKER
Cyclopterus lumpus L.

a female, 32 cm
b male, 34 cm, in March
c principal food
d utilisation

c

sandhoppers

comb-jellies

d

gobies

roe

The lumpsucker has the ventral fins modified to form a suction disc. Their skin is scaleless and there is no swimbladder.

The dorsal fin is situated far back behind a distinct dorsal ridge and the skin of the body is covered with small bony denticles and longitudinal rows of large bony thorns. The females have a taller dorsal ridge and smaller pectoral fins than the males.

Length 30 cm in the males, maximum 50 cm (1–5 kg) in the females. Lives on hard, stony ground in depths of 20–200 m, sometimes also pelagically. In February-May they collect in pairs in shallow, coastal waters, where the females each lay some 200,000 yellowish-red eggs which later become greenish. The eggs are guarded by the male until they hatch into tadpole-shaped young fish 6–7 mm. These spend the summer in the seaweed zone, and move into deeper water at the beginning of the winter. Lumpsuckers feed on crustaceans, small fishes and comb-jellies.

They are taken as an incidental catch in fixed nets. Marketed fresh, smoked or salted. The watery, gelatinous flesh is no longer in demand. Some 1,000 tons are landed annually in Denmark, where the roes are treated with salt and other substances, including a black dye, and then marketed as a kind of caviar.

138 b

14 cm

139. SEA SNAIL

Liparis liparis

10 cm

140. MONTAGU'S SEA SNAIL

Liparis montagui

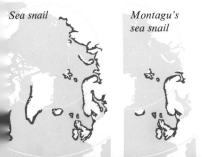

Sea snail

Montagu's
sea snail

139. Sea snail

Liparis liparis (L.)

Characteristics: Dorsal and anal fins very long, and both connected with the caudal fin. Body shaped like a tadpole, with soft slimy skin, and no scales. The ventral fins are modified to form a round adhesion disc. Swimbladder absent. Coloration very variable, being yellowish, reddish or brown according to the surroundings.

Maximum length 15 cm. Lives in the algal zone and spawns in winter. The eggs are laid on algae or polyp colonies and take 6-8 weeks to hatch. Sea snails feed on small crustaceans.

140. Montagu's sea snail

Liparis montagui (Donovan)

Characteristics: Dorsal and anal fins not fused with the caudal fin.

Maximum length 12 cm. Very similar in appearance and habits to the preceding species.

141. Three-spined stickleback

Gasterosteus aculeatus L.

Seldom longer than 7 cm, maximum length in the sea 11 cm, in fresh water 8 cm. The marine forms live in coastal waters, and in somewhat deeper water in the winter months. In the spring the male develops his bright courtship coloration and starts to build a nest on the bottom, using plant fragments which he cements together with a secretion from his kidneys. When this has been completed he drives several females, one by one, into the nest where each lays some of her 100–400 eggs. These are immediately fertilised by the male. After spawning the female is driven from the nest and the male alone takes over the task of caring for and guarding the spawn (300–1,000 eggs). He repairs the nest, drives away spawn-robbers and fans fresh water over the eggs with his pectoral fins. The eggs hatch in 4–27 days according to the temperature. The young fish remain in or near the nest for about a week before moving off, sometimes in large shoals, to hunt for tiny prey among the vegetation. Sticklebacks are sexually mature after one year and live for three years at the most. They feed on fish eggs and fry, small crustaceans, worms etc. Outside the spawning season they live in shoals.

Sticklebacks are themselves eaten by salmon, eels, cod and herons. They can be caught in shallow water in fine-mesh nets.

142. Ten-spined stickleback

Pungitius pungitius (L.)

Up to 7 cm long. Lives mainly in fresh water, sometimes entering brackish water. In contrast to the three-spined stickleback the male builds a nest suspended in water plants, above the bottom. They become sexually mature at the end of the 1st year, and spawning takes place in spring. They feed on animal plankton, and to a lesser extent on small bottom-living animals. Of no economic importance.

143. Sea stickleback

Spinachia spinachia (L.)

Snout pointed, tail long and thin. On the back, 14–17 free spiny rays. Front of body brassy-yellow in the male, with larger pectoral fins than in the female. Coloration

newly hatched larva, 6 m

brownish or greenish, varying according to the surroundings.

Length 10–15 cm, maximum 20 cm. Lives singly or in pairs in the algal zone. The male builds a nest of algal fragments, stuck together with a kidney secretion. In May-June the female lays 150–200 eggs in the nest and these are tended and guarded by the male. The young grow fast and are sexually mature in the following spring.

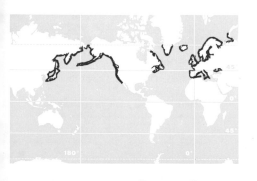

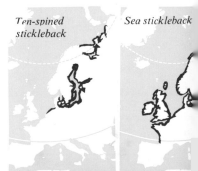

Ten-spined stickleback

Sea stickleback

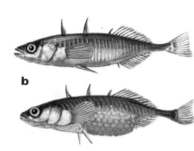

141. THREE-SPINED STICKLEBACK

Gasterosteus aculeatus

- 6 cm
- male and gravid female in breeding dress
- c nest

a

b

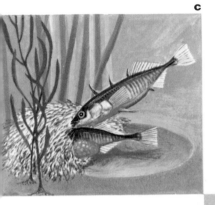

c

5 cm

142. TEN-SPINED STICKLEBACK

Pungitius pungitius

143. SEA STICKLEBACK

Spinachia spinachia

a 15 cm
b nest

b

a

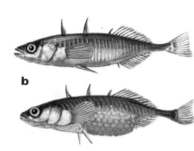

FLATFISHES

The pelagic larvae of flatfishes are symmetrical and swim upright in the water, like ordinary fishes. It is only in the course of further development that one eye moves over the top of the head and on to the other side of the body. The young fish then start to lie and to swim on one side and at a certain length they begin to live on the bottom (see fig. 154b, p. 187). Some species and individuals have the eyes on the right side, others on the left side the body. The side with eyes is dark pigmented, the other side usually colou less. The dorsal and anal fins are lon both with jointed rays. In many speci there is an anal thorn in front of t anal fin. There is no swimbladder.

Flatfishes live (as adults) on the botto and feed on bivalve molluscs, crustacear worms, echinoderms and small botto living fishes.

They are caught in trawls and sei nets and by hook and line.

Key to the main groups

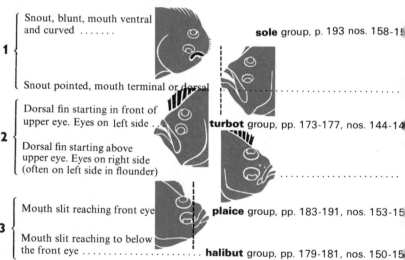

1 {
Snout, blunt, mouth ventral and curved .... **sole** group, p. 193 nos. 158-1

Snout pointed, mouth terminal or dorsal ....

2 {
Dorsal fin starting in front of upper eye. Eyes on left side ... **turbot** group, pp. 173-177, nos. 144-14

Dorsal fin starting above upper eye. Eyes on right side (often on left side in flounder) ....

3 {
Mouth slit reaching front eye **plaice** group, pp. 183-191, nos. 153-15

Mouth slit reaching to below the front eye .... **halibut** group, pp. 179-181, nos. 150-15

144. Turbot

Scophthalmus maximus (L.)

Body almost circular. Eye side scaleless, but with large bony tubercles. In the North Sea reaching a length of *c*. 30 cm in 5 years. Maximum length 90–100 cm (*c*. 12 kg). Seldom over 50 cm in the Baltic Sea. Males smaller than females.

Turbots live on sandy, rocky or mixed bottoms in depths of 20–70 m. They feed mainly on other bottom-living fishes (sand-eels, gobies etc), and also, to a lesser exten on the larger crustaceans and bivalves.

The turbot becomes sexually mature

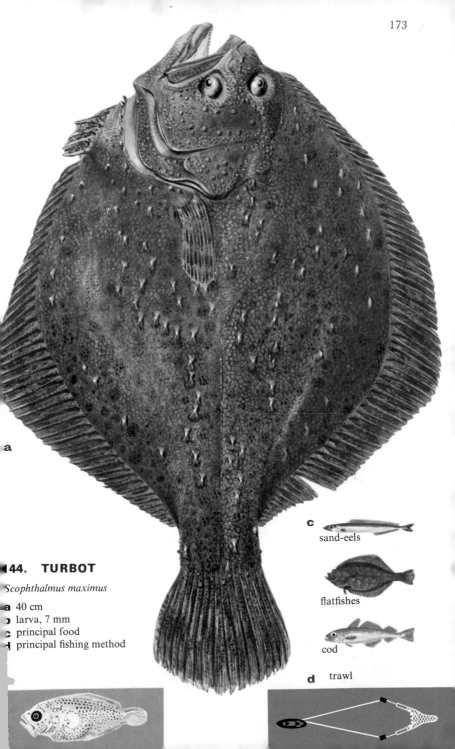

44. TURBOT

Scophthalmus maximus

a 40 cm
b larva, 7 mm
c principal food
d principal fishing method

c sand-eels

flatfishes

cod

d trawl

its 5th year and in most parts of its range spawns in April-August in depths of 10–40 m. A single female produces 10–15 million eggs. The larvae are at first pelagic, and move down to the bottom in shallow coastal waters when 2·5 cm long. By autumn the young, then 8–10 cm long, move gradually into deeper water. In the Baltic Sea the males are sexually mature at 15 cm, the females at 20 cm, and the young grow more slowly. It is remarkable that in all areas the males appear to be in the majority.

This is a valuable edible fish which fetches a high price on the market. It is caught in trawls, seines and by line fishing. The total annual catch in western Europe is 6,000–7,000 tons, of which Britain takes c. 1,500 tons, Denmark 1,000 tons. Germany, Belgium and Holland each 500–900 tons. Turbot are also caught in the Mediterranean and Black Seas. By international agreement the minimum length landed is 30 cm.

Turbot have been successfully introduced to New Zealand.

145. Brill

Scophthalmus rhombus (L.)

Thinner and more slender than the turbot. Skin with small, smooth scales, without bony tubercles.

Brill reach a length of up to 75 cm in the Mediterranean, but rarely more than 60 cm in the North Sea or c. 35 cm in the Baltic Sea. They live on sandy or mixed bottoms in depths of 5–50 m, and feed on bottom-living fishes and larger crustaceans. Spawning takes place in March-April in depths of 10–20 m, and the larvae move down to the bottom when 12–25 mm long. The young fish remain in shallow water for 1–2 years.

The minimum size allowed to be landed is 30 cm. The total annual European catch is c. 2,000 tons.

146. Scaldfish

Arnoglossus laterna (Walbaum)

Distinctive features: Body slender, translucent and shaped like a sole. Behind the ventrals two backward curved thorns. Maximum length in the Mediterranean c. 25 cm, in the North Sea rarely up to 19 cm. Lives on mixed bottoms in depths of 10–100 m and feeds on gobies, crustaceans etc. Spawns in May-August.

Of no importance to the fisheries, on account of its small size.

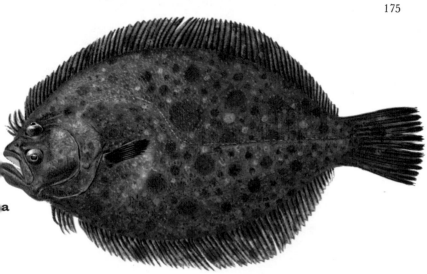

a

145. BRILL

Scophthalmus rhombus

a 32 cm
b principal food

b

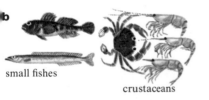

small fishes

crustaceans

15 cm

146. SCALDFISH

Arnoglossus laterna

147. Megrim

Lepidorhombus whiffiagonis (Walbaum)

Distinctive features: Eyes and mouth large. Smooth scales on the blind side. The dorsal fin starts about half way between the tip of the snout and the upper eye. Body thin, translucent.

Rarely longer than 50 cm. Lives on mixed ground in depths of 100–400 m, but is sometimes also found free-swimming. Feeds on small bottom-living fishes and spawns in March-June.

Taken in the trawl, mostly south of the English Channel. The total annual European catch is *c.* 20,000 tons, of which Spain lands *c.* 10,000 tons and Britain *c.* 1,400 tons.

Minimum size allowed to be landed: 25 cm.

spawns in April-August. Norwegian topknots are probably commoner and more widely distributed than has hitherto been thought. Because of their small size they are often overlooked and also they slip through the trawl meshes.

149. Topknot

Zeugopterus punctatus (Bloch)

Distinctive features: Scales on the eye side with fine, spiny outgrowths, which feel like rough fur.

Rarely longer than 25 cm. Lives on stony or rocky ground in the algal zone and feeds on small fishes and crustaceans. Spawns in March-June.

Of no economic importance, on account of its small size.

148. Norwegian topknot

Phrynorhombus norvegicus (Günther)

Distinctive features: Scales on the blind side rough. The dorsal fin starts above the upper eye. The markings on the eye side are arranged in irregular transverse bands.

This is the smallest of the North European flatfish species. Maximum length 10–12 cm. So far as is known, it lives mainly on stony ground. It feeds on worms, small crustaceans and fish eggs, and

28 cm

147. MEGRIM

Lepidorhombus whiffiagonis

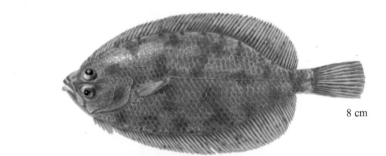

8 cm

148. NORWEGIAN TOPKNOT

Phrynorhombus norvegicus

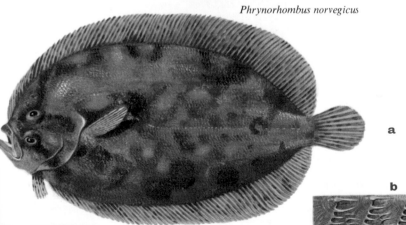

a

b

49. TOPKNOT

Zeugopterus punctatus

a 10 cm
b scales, × 8

150. Halibut

Hippoglossus hippoglossus (L.)

Body slender, with the eyes on the right side. The dorsal fin starts above the upper eye. Lateral line with a marked curve in the front third of the body. The largest of the flatfish species.

Maximum length 3–4 m (*c.* 300 kg). Lives up to 40–50 years. Specimens over 2 m long are very rarely caught nowadays.

A roaming, bottom-living fish, which lives in depths of 50–2,000 m, in waters with a temperature of 3–9°C and a high salinity. Is also frequently found free-swimming. Occasionally, a few individuals move into shallow water.

Spawning takes place in December–April, close to the bottom in depths of 300–1,000 m, at a temperature of 5–7°C. The principal grounds are off the Norwegian coast north of Aalesund, along the edge of the Continental Slope from Scotland and the Faeroes to Greenland, and in the waters around Newfoundland. The female lays about 2 million eggs (diameter 3–4 mm) which drift in fairly deep water for 9–16 days and hatch into larvae that are 6·5–7 mm long. At a length of 30–35 mm they metamorphose into the adult 'flatfish' form, and when 4 cm long the young fish move down to the bottom near the coast. They spend their first 2–4 years in depths of 30–100 m. After 1 year they are 8–15 cm long, after 2 years 18–33 cm. The females grow considerably faster than the males. They become sexually mature in their 7th to 18th year (off the Norwegian coast usually when they are 12–13 years old); at this point the males are *c.* 110 cm (18 kg), the females 135 cm (35 kg).

After spawning the adults migrate to their feeding grounds in shallow water not far from the coast, where they hunt for small fishes. Some of the Norwegian population reach the Barents Sea. Marking experiments have shown that certain individuals migrate over long distances.

The halibut is a very voracious predator which feeds mainly on other fishes (cod, haddock, pogge, sand-eels, herring, capelin), but also takes cephalopods, large crustaceans and other bottom-living animals. During the winter months when it is living at great depths it feeds very largely on the deep-sea prawn, *Pandalus borealis.*

Halibut are mainly caught on hook and line, but they also appear in the trawl. Special halibut nets are used to catch them on their spawning grounds off the Norwegian coast.

On account of the slow growth rate and the late onset of sexual maturity, halibut populations can be seriously affected by overfishing. Various measures have therefore been taken, particularly by the Norwegians, to define spawning grounds and seasons when fishing is prohibited. In Norway the minimum size that can be landed is 50 cm.

Halibut flesh is very well-flavoured and at its best in autumn and winter. It is marketed fresh, frozen, salted or smoked.

The annual landings for the North Atlantic amount to *c.* 10,000 tons, of which Norway takes 3,000 tons, Britain and Canada each 2,000 tons, and Iceland 1,000 tons.

There is a closely related species in the northern part of the Pacific Ocean.

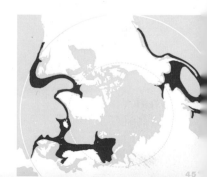

150. HALIBUT

Hippoglossus hippoglossus

a 45 cm
b larva, 22 mm
c principal food
d utilisation
e principal fishing methods

a

b

c

cod family

herring

sand-eels

pogge

Dublin Bay prawn

cephalopods

d

fresh fish

hook

trawl

e

151. Greenland halibut

Reinhardtius hippoglossoides (Walbaum)

Eyes on the right side. Less asymmetric than the other flatfishes. The blind side is brownish or bluish, and the left eye only moves round (during development) to the edge of the head. The dorsal fin starts behind the left eye. Lateral line almost straight. Sexually mature in the 9th-10th year at the earliest, when 60–70 cm long. The males are mostly up to 80 cm long (6–7 kg), the females up to 100 cm (18 kg). Maximum length 120 cm, maximum weight *c*. 45 kg.

An arctic species living in depths of 200–2,000 m, which swims in the upright position (like an ordinary fish) and is often found in open water. The growth, spawning grounds and migrations have been little investigated. Spawns in April-June in 700–2,000 m at a temperature of 3–5°C in the western Barents Sea and the southern Davis Strait. The eggs (diameter 4–4·5 mm) float freely in deep water, as do the transparent larvae (length 10–16 mm). Metamorphosis is complete at a length of 60–85 mm and the young then move down to depths of 50–200 m. They move into even deeper water when 12–25 cm long. Greenland halibut feed on deep-sea prawns, Vahl's eelpout, capelin, small cod, etc. The dark pigmentation on the blind side of the body reflects the more pelagic habits of this flatfish.

This species is caught on long lines in depths of 700–1,000 m. The most important fishing grounds are the steep parts below the Continental Shelf and the banks off Tromsø, Finnmark and Greenland. Marketed as fresh fish or deep-frozen.

A proportion of the catch is salted a smoked.

Total catch in the North Atlan 100,000–140,000 tons.

There is subspecies in the northe part of the Pacific Ocean.

152. Long rough dab

Hippoglossoides platessoides (Fabricius)

Eyes on the right side of the body. T dorsal fin starts above the left eye. Late line almost straight. Mouth large, sca rough.

Maximum length *c*. 50 cm, longev 19 years at the most, but rarely ov 40 cm long or more than 10 years c (weight *c*. 700 g). Lives on soft ground depths of 10–400 m. Spawns in Janua May in the North Sea, in March-July the Barents Sea. The female produ 50,000–300,000 floating eggs (diame 1·3–3·2 mm) in depths of 150–200 m. T larvae are pelagic until they reach a leng of 20–30 mm, and then, even before me morphosis is complete, they move down the bottom in depths of 40–100 m. In North Sea this species becomes sexua mature in the 2nd-3rd year at the earli (when the fish are *c*. 25 cm long), but in t Barents Sea, where the growth rate is mu lower, not until the 7th-12th year at a leng of 30–45 cm. They spawn throughout th range. The diet consists of small c sand-eels, gobies, worms, small brittlesta crustaceans, molluscs.

This is an unwanted by-product fr trawl or long line, for the flesh is wate and poor in quality and quantity.

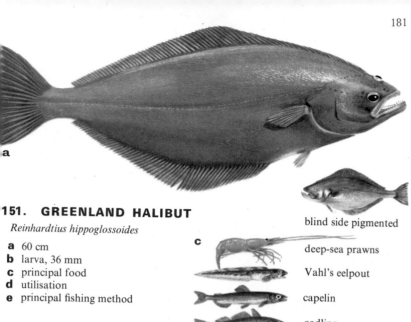

a

151. GREENLAND HALIBUT

Reinhardtius hippoglossoides

a 60 cm
b larva, 36 mm
c principal food
d utilisation
e principal fishing method

blind side pigmented

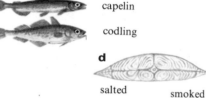

deep-sea prawns

Vahl's eelpout

capelin

codling

b

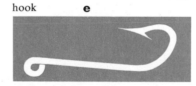

d

salted   smoked

hook   e

52. LONG
OUGH DAB

Hippoglossoides platessoides

32 cm

Danish Baltic Sea fishing boat

153. Dab

Limanda limanda (L.)

Lateral line with a semicircular curve above the pectoral fin. Scales on the eye side rough.

Rarely over 40 cm long (*c.* 720 g), and usually under 30 cm. Lives mainly on sandy ground in slightly shallower water than the plaice. Particularly abundant in the North Sea.

Spawns near the coast in January-August, earliest off the French coast, but later (June-July) in the Barents Sea. In the Baltic, spawning extends over the period April-August. In the southern North Sea spawning takes place in depths of 20–40 m, but somewhat deeper in the southern Baltic. The female produces 50,000–150,000 pelagic eggs (diameter 0·7–1 mm) which hatch in 7–14 days into larvae that are 2·5 mm long. When about 14 mm long the larvae move down to the bottom in depths of 6–70 m, before they have, in fact, metamorphosed into 'flatfish'. The rate of growth varies considerably according to the locality: in the Barents Sea they become sexually mature in the 4th-5th year at a length of 22-24 cm, in the North Sea in the 2nd-3rd year when 15-20 cm long, or in a few individuals when only 10 cm long.

Dabs feed principally on brittlestars, small sea-urchins, hermit-crabs, sand-hoppers, worms and molluscs, and to a lesser extent on sand-eels, gobies and (in the Barents Sea) on capelin. As their diet are so similar, dabs are in many places serious food competitors of the more valuable plaice.

They are usually taken as an incidental catch in trawl, seine and fixed net fisheries. They are marketed as fresh fish packed in ice, or more commonly as deep-frozen fillets together with those of the lemon sole and plaice. The North Sea Convention has laid down the minimum length to be landed as 20 cm.

The annual catches are: Denmark 4,000 tons, France 4,000 tons, Britain *c.* 2,000 tons, Holland 2,000 tons, Germany and Belgium each 200–500 tons.

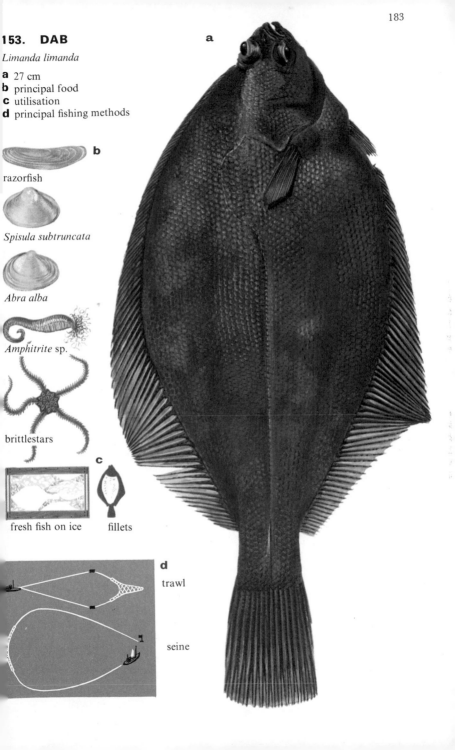

153. DAB

Limanda limanda

a 27 cm
b principal food
c utilisation
d principal fishing methods

b

razorfish

Spisula subtruncata

Abra alba

Amphitrite sp.

brittlestars

c

fresh fish on ice   fillets

d
trawl

seine

154. Plaice

Pleuronectes platessa L.

Distinctive features: Smooth, with small scales. A ridge with 4–7 bony knobs runs from the eyes back over the head. Eye side grey-brown with reddish spots (with pale edges in old specimens). Hybrids between plaice and flounder are common in the southern Danish Belt (see flounder, p. 188).

Maximum length 95 cm, weight 7 kg, longevity *c.* 50 years; such large specimens are however very rarely caught. Average length 25–40 cm.

A bottom-living species on mixed mud and sandy grounds from the shore to depths of 200 m. Most adult plaice occur in depths of 10–50 m, the young usually in shallower water. There are numerous local races, which are characterised by the number of fin rays and vertebrae. Thus, one can distinguish between a Baltic and a North Sea plaice. The transition zones have a mixture of local forms. The size and form of the body are primarily dependent upon the conditions for growth in the locality concerned. The plaice shown on the opposite page comes from the Danish Belt where food is plentiful; it has a broader body and a smaller head than the North Sea form.

Plaice spawn in winter. In the North Sea the principal spawning grounds are off the Belgian-Dutch coast, the east coast of Britain, on the Great Fisher Bank and north-west of Heligoland, in the Baltic Sea off Bornholm and Bohuslän, and in the Kattegat and Danish Belt. They also spawn along the Norwegian coast, in the Barents Sea and off south-west Iceland, but are less common in Faeroese waters.

Spawning takes place at a temperature of about 6°C, in the North Sea from January to June in depths of 20–40 m, in the western Baltic from November to June in depths of 60–90 m. A salinity of at least 10–12 parts per thousand is necessary for the eggs to be able to float freely in the water. In a water of lower salinity the eggs will quickly sink, so that

an insufficient number become fertilised. In the Baltic Sea only the western part has a sufficiently high salinity for a successful spawning.

Off Iceland the plaice spawns in March–April, in the Barents Sea from March to May, partly in depths of 160–200 m at a temperature of only 2–2.5°C, and partly also in shallower water.

The number of eggs produced varies according to the size of the female, from 50,000 to 520,000. The eggs have a diameter of 1.6 mm, and they float in the water. In the North Sea they hatch in 10–20 days, but in the Barents Sea they take up to a month, according to the temperature.

The newly hatched larvae are 6 mm long and at first they have the normal symmetrical fish shape. They are pelagic and feed on the microscopic larvae of worms and gastropods. After 1–2 months, at a length of *c.* 10 mm, they start to metamorphose: the left eye moves across the upper edge of the head and the young start to swim with the left side facing downwards.

Metamorphosis is complete at a length of 12–14 mm, and the young fish then start to live on the bottom in shallow coastal waters. The side facing the light becomes darkly pigmented, whereas the blind side is colourless.

At first the young plaice feed mainly on small worms and crustaceans, but with increasing age they start to take larger food.

Danish seine boat from the Belt area.

154. PLAICE

Pleuronectes platessa

a 36 cm

a

animals; by autumn they are eating large bristle-worms, sandhoppers and thin-shelled bivalves, which also form the principal diet of the adults; they are then *c.* 7–12 cm long and move slowly into deeper water for the winter.

As in the other flatfish species, the growth of plaice is very largely dependent upon the temperature, the amount of available food and the density of the population. On the west coast of Jutland the population is sometimes so dense that the rate of growth falls steeply. Attempts have therefore been made to transfer young fish from overpopulated areas into the Belt and Limfjord (Denmark) in order to get better growth and a high yield. Recent investigations have, however, shown that such transplants are scarcely economic.

Plaice feed very little during the winter and it is not until the spring that the young fish move back again to their feeding grounds in shallow water. Like flounders, plaice are particularly active at night when they may be found in very shallow water.

In the North Sea the males are sexually mature in their 3rd-4th year at a length of 18–26 cm, the females in the 6th year at a length of *c.* 35 cm, but in the Barents Sea the males in their 6th-9th year (30–40 cm) and the females in their 7th-13th year (34–47 cm). Tagging experiments have shown that plaice can cover long distances during their spawning migrations. In some cases daily runs of 18–30 km have been recorded.

Plaice are mainly caught in trawls and seine nets, but considerable numbers are also taken in set nets or even accidentally by hook and line. In the North Sea area only those over 25 cm can be landed. In some areas larger minimum sizes and special regulations to protect the breeding fish have been introduced. Plaice are mostly marketed as fresh fish packed in ice, but some of the catch is filleted, or even smoked. The skin can be tanned.

The plaice is one of the most important commercial fishes. The annual European catch is 150,000–170,000 tons, of which Denmark lands 39,000–53,000 tons, Britain

tags

35,000–45,000 tons, Holland 40,000–45,000 tons, Belgium 4,000–5,000 tons, Germany 3,800–4,400 tons, Iceland 1,000–4,400 tons, Sweden 1,100 tons, Ireland 1,000 tons and Norway 900 tons.

154. PLAICE

b egg and larvae, × 5
c otolith of a 4 year-old plaice, × 4
d principal food
e principal fishing methods
f utilisation

Egg (1·6–2·1 mm) shortly before the larva hatches

3 pelagic larvae
  7 mm.........8–12 days
8·5 mm........20–25 days
 11 mm........35–40 days

bottom stage:
12·5 mm........45–50 days

razorfish

d

Spisula subtruncata

Abra alba

tellins.

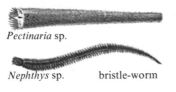

Pectinaria sp.

Nephthys sp.   bristle-worm

c

f

deep-frozen fillets

fresh fish on ice

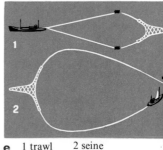

1

2

e   1 trawl   2 seine

155. Flounder

Platichthys flesus (L.)

Distinctive features: body surface rough particularly along the lateral line and at the base of the dorsal and anal fins. Lateral line only slightly curved above the pectoral fins. Flounders usually have the eyes on the right side but in some places up to a third of the population may have them on the left. Hybrids may be produced in areas where flounders and plaice spawn at the same time, e.g. in the southern Danish Belt; such hybrids have a somewhat smoother skin than the flounder and red spots that are not so conspicuous as those of the plaice. There are 6 geographical subspecies within the distribution range of the flounder.

Maximum length 50 cm, but individuals over 30 cm are very rarely caught. Flounders range from the tidal zone to depths of 25 m, the youngest stages being in the shallowest water. In summer they tend to live in estuaries, lagoons and fjords and some individuals penetrate far up the rivers. With the onset of colder weather most of them leave the shallow brackish water and move to the deeper, warmer and saltier sea water. Spawning takes place in depths of 20–40 m, in the southern North Sea from February to May, off the Kola Peninsula from April to June and in the Black Sea from January to March.

In the western Baltic Sea the flounders spawn in depths of 40–100 m, in areas with a salinity of at least 10 parts per thousand. In lower salinities the eggs sink to the bottom and mostly die or are not fertilised. The female produces 400,000 to 2 million pelagic eggs (diameter 0·8–1·4 mm). When the surface temperature is *c.* 10°C these hatch in 5–7 days. On hatching the transparent larvae are only 3 mm long and they live a pelagic life until 7–10 mm long. The young fish move down to the bottom in shallow, coastal waters before they are fully metamorphosed, and for the first few weeks they feed on microscopic crustaceans. Growth is dependent, amongst other things, on the density of the population and the amount of available food. At the end of their first year of life the young flounders off Bornholm are only *c.* 4 cm long, but those in the Kattegat are 13 cm. Independent of their size, the males become sexually mature when 3 years old, the females when 4 years old; at this point they will be 20–35 cm long.

Flounders feed on worms, sandhoppers, sea-slaters, prawns, bivalves, gobies and sand-eels. The older fish feed mainly on molluscs and small fishes, whereas the young feed more on small crustaceans. A 24-hour rhythm can be observed in their feeding behaviour: they spend most of the day (especially the larger flounders) buried in the sand, but become very active at night and move into shallower water to feed.

Flounders are caught in traps, fixed nets and seines. Most countries have introduced a minimum size and a closed period. They are marketed fresh or smoked.

The annual European catch is *c.* 10,000 tons, of which Denmark lands 4,000–5,000 tons, Germany 1,000 tons, Holland 700 tons, Sweden 500 tons and Britain 200 tons.

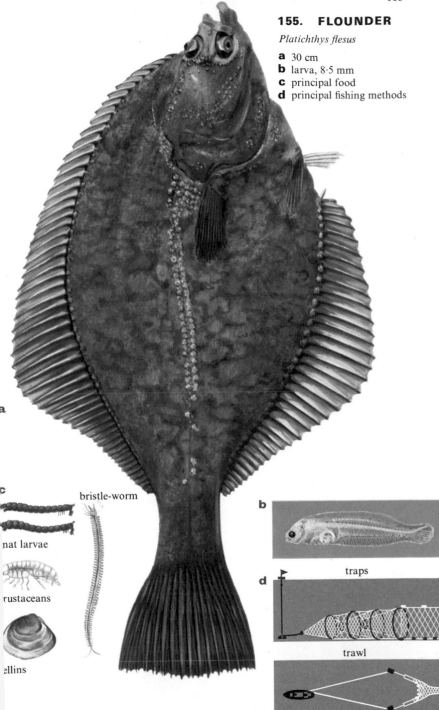

189

155. FLOUNDER

Platichthys flesus

a 30 cm
b larva, 8·5 mm
c principal food
d principal fishing methods

bristle-worm

nat larvae

rustaceans

ellins

b

traps

d

trawl

156. Lemon sole

Microstomus kitt (Walbaum)

Distinctive features: Without an anal thorn. Lateral line almost straight, with only a slight curve above the pectoral fin. Eye side smooth, red-brown to yellow-brown with darker marble. Head and mouth very small. Body fleshy.

Lemon soles are stationary, bottom-living fishes and their growth depends very much on local conditions. In the North Sea they reach a length of 20–30 cm in the 5th year. Maximum length 45 cm. They live on hard, stony or rocky bottoms in depths of 20–150 m, and become sexually mature at the end of the 3rd-4th year. Spawning takes place in March-September in depths of *c.* 100 m. The eggs hatch into larvae (length 4·5–5·5 mm) which remain in the open water until autumn. They start to become asymmetrical when 15–16 mm long, but do not move down to the bottom in relatively deep water until 3 cm long.

Lemon soles feed mainly on crustaceans, scale-worms, barnacles and chitons.

They are caught, mainly in winter, in trawls and seines or as a by-product of, e.g. the prawn fishery. The most important fishing grounds are off Iceland and the Faeroes, in the northern North Sea and to the west and south of Britain. The annual European catch is *c.* 10,000 tons, of which Britain alone lands *c.* 5,000 tons.

The minimum size for landing is 25 cm.

157. Witch

Glyptocephalus cynoglossus (L.)

Distinctive features: Body elongated; anal spine present; lateral line almost completely straight. Eye side rough, and a uniform grey-brown. Pectoral fin on the eye side with a black tip. Mouth very small.

Maximum length *c.* 55 cm. In the North Sea the males reach a length of 29 cm in the 5th year, the females *c.* 33 cm. The witch lives on soft bottoms in depths of 100–400 m and at temperatures of 5–7°C it is a characteristic fish of the deep Norwegian fjords, of the Faeroes area and of the slopes off the Norwegian coast.

They become sexually mature in the 4th-5th year, and spawn in May-September. Like the adults, the young fish also live in considerable depths. The development of the egg and larva has not been fully investigated. They feed mainly on worms, molluscs and small crustaceans.

This is a valuable commercial fish taken in trawl and seine off Bohuslan, off the Norwegian coast, in the northern North Sea and off Iceland and Ireland. Some are also taken in prawn nets.

The annual European catch is *c.* 4,000 tons, of which Britain lands *c.* 1,500 tons. Canada lands *c.* 4,000 tons from the western part of the species' range.

Minimum size to be landed: 28 cm.

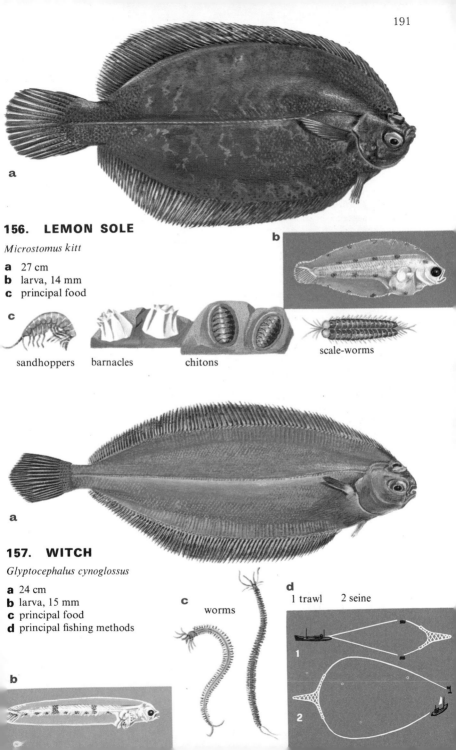

156. LEMON SOLE

Microstomus kitt

a 27 cm
b larva, 14 mm
c principal food

sandhoppers   barnacles   chitons   scale-worms

157. WITCH

Glyptocephalus cynoglossus

a 24 cm
b larva, 15 mm
c principal food
d principal fishing methods

worms

d 1 trawl   2 seine

158. Sole

Solea solea (L.)

Distinctive features: Both pectoral fins well-developed. Nasal openings on the blind side small, and widely separated from one another.

Average length 30–40 cm, weight *c.* 320 g, average longevity 4–8 years. Maximum length *c.* 60 cm (3 kg, age over 20 years). Lives mainly on sandy or muddy ground in depths of 10–60 m.

Soles spawn from April to July in the southern North Sea (and at some places in the Skagerrak and Kattegat), from March to April off the coasts of Ireland and southern England, and as early as February in the Mediterranean. Spawning takes place in shallow coastal waters with a temperature of 6–12°C. The female produces 100,000–150,000 eggs (diameter 1·3–1·5 mm) which drift freely in the water. At 9–10°C they hatch in *c.* 10 days into pelagic larvae which are 3·6 mm long. These metamorphose into 'flatfish' when 12–15 mm long and the young fish then move down to live on the bottom in shallow coastal (and also brackish) waters; later on they move into deeper water. Soles reach a length of 8–15 cm in their first year, and become sexually mature in the 3rd-5th year when 25–30 cm long; the males are somewhat smaller than the females.

Soles hunt for food at night, taking thin-shelled bivalves, bristle-worms, crustaceans and to a lesser extent small fishes (gobies, sand-eels). By day they usually lie buried in the sand.

Soles are caught in trawls and seines, and also in fixed nets that are laid out against the direction of the current. The minimum size (North Sea Convention) to be landed is 24 cm. On account of its firm flesh this is one of the most highly esteemed of the flatfishes.

The annual European catch is 34,000–45,000 tons, of which Holland lands 15,000–20,000 tons, France 5,000 tons, Belgium 4,000 tons, Britain and Denmark 2,000 tons each, and Germany 1,000–2,000 tons.

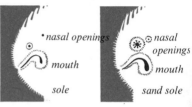

The sand sole, *Pegusa lascaris*, a closely related species that is often confused with the sole, occurs from the English Channel to the Mediterranean. It differs from the sole in having the first nasal opening (on the blind side) much enlarged.

159. Solenette

Buglossidium luteum (Risso)

Distinctive features: pectoral fins very small. Every 6th or 7th ray of the dorsal and anal fins is black.

Maximum length 12–13 cm. The solenette lives on shallow sandy bottoms in depths of 5–20 m and spawns in March-July. The pelagic eggs (diameter *c.* 1 mm) hatch in 5–6 days into pelagic larvae that are 2 mm long. The young fish move down to the bottom when metamorphosis is complete and they are *c.* 10 mm long. The males become sexually mature at a length of 6–7 cm, the females at 7–8 cm. Solenettes feed on small worms and crustaceans.

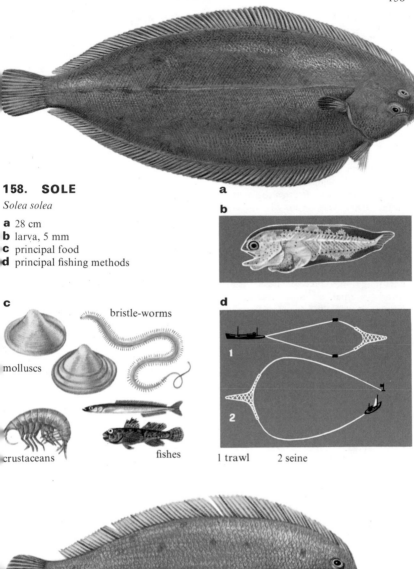

158. SOLE

Solea solea

a 28 cm
b larva, 5 mm
c principal food
d principal fishing methods

a

b

c

molluscs

bristle-worms

crustaceans

fishes

d

1 trawl   2 seine

159. SOLENETTE

Buglossidium luteum

10 cm

160. Sunfish

Mola mola (L.)

Distinctive features: Body short and tall, with strong lateral compression. No ventral fins. Caudal fin replaced by a stiff fringe of skin. Dorsal and anal fins modified to form long 'paddles' which can only be moved from side to side. Skin scaleless and leathery, and overlying a thick, fibrous layer. Mouth small. Can produce grinding sounds (?by means of the jaws).

Maximum length *c.* 3 m (*c.* 1,400 kg). Distributed throughout the world in warm and temperate seas. It often drifts at the surface while lying on its side, or swims upright and so close to the surface that the dorsal fin projects above the water. Spawning takes place in, among other places, the Sargasso Sea, the female producing some 300 million eggs! The larvae have long spines and a well-developed tail with a normal caudal fin which later disappears, while the dorsal and anal fins retain their characteristic appearance.

Sunfish feed on animal plankton, eel larvae and small deep-sea fishes. They appear as occasional visitors in autumn in the North Sea and Skagerrak. A close relative, the truncated sunfish, *Ranzania laevis* (80 cm), is sometimes seen off the British coasts.

161. Angler

Lophius piscatorius L.

Average length 40–60 cm, maximum length *c.* 1·7 m (30–40 kg). Occurs on sandy and muddy bottoms from the coast down to depths of 1,000 m. Spawns in April-June in areas to the north, west and south of the British Isles in depths of over 400 m. The female lays *c.* one million eggs which lie embedded in a violet, mucus band 10 m long and 15–45 cm broad. This mass of spawn drifts freely in the water, is torn apart by the waves and becomes widely distributed by the currents. The larvae live a pelagic life until they are 6–8 cm long, and then move down to the bottom in fairly shallow water.

The angler is well adapted as a bottom-living fish which lures inquisitive prey by means of the movable first dorsal fin ray which has a fleshy piece of skin at its tip. As soon as the victim is close enough it is snapped up by the angler's enormous mouth. The pointed teeth curve inwards and this makes it easy to swallow the prey and also prevents it from escaping. Anglers feed on conger eels, gurnards, rays etc, and can also take diving birds. They themselves are landed as a by-product from the trawl and long line fisheries. The annual European catch is 35,000 tons, of which Britain takes *c.* 3,500 tons, Spain 13,000 tons, France 14,000 tons, and other countries 200–500 tons each. It is marketed without the head and skin. The first insulin was extracted from its pancreas.

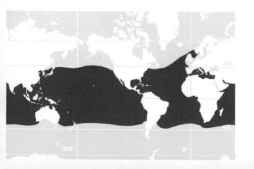

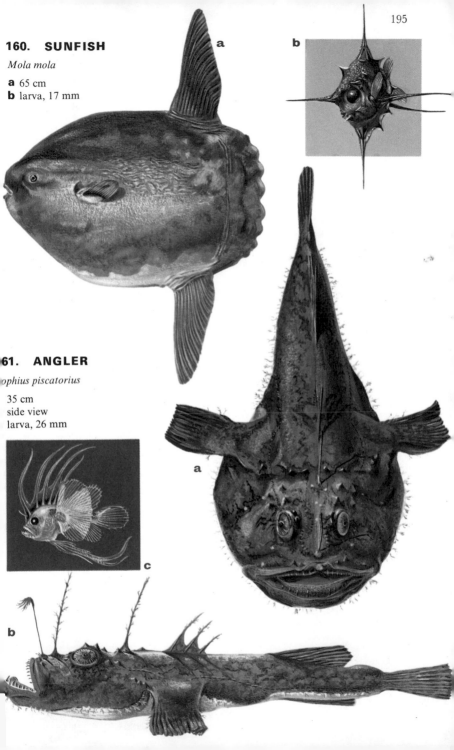

160. SUNFISH

Mola mola

a 65 cm
b larva, 17 mm

161. ANGLER

ophius piscatorius

35 cm
side view
larva, 26 mm

162. Shrimp

Crangon vulgaris Fabricius

Body grey, transparent, without a rostrum. Maximum length 8 cm. Lives in depths of 0–20 m, often in enormous numbers in shallow water during the summer. The female lays 2,000–14,000 eggs two or three times a year, and carries these about attached to her abdomen. The larvae are free-swimming until they are about 10 mm long. Shrimps are hermaphrodites, which function 1–2 years as males, and subsequently as females. They seldom live for more than 3–4 years. The diet consists of invertebrates, detritus, algae.

They play an important part in coastal fisheries, and are caught in trawls (beam trawls), worked from small motor boats, and with push nets and traps. Larger shrimps are cooked and shelled, and then canned, the smaller ones (mainly males) are dried (for fodder and fertilizer).

163. Deep-sea prawn

Pandalus borealis Krøyer

Lives on soft bottoms in depths of 50–500 m and at temperatures of 0–8°C. They move towards the surface at night. Hermaphrodites. During their first two years (in the Skagerrak) or four years (off Greenland and Spitzbergen) the male germ cells mature; the female cells do so later on. Mating takes place in the autumn,

the eggs being fertilised within the maternal body. After the 1,000–3,000 eggs are laid they are carried around by the female for the whole winter (off Greenland for even up to 9 months), before they hatch into pelagic larvae. The adults feed on small crustaceans and worms. They themselves are eaten by numerous enemies, and form an important food for fishes.

Of considerable economic importance. Norway lands 10,000 tons a year, Denmark 4,000–6,000 tons.

164. Baltic prawn

Leander adspersus (Rathke)

The females reach a length of up to 8 cm, the males being considerably smaller. Live in the algal zone, particularly in sheltered bays and fjords. The female lays 300–2,500 eggs once or twice a year and carries them around on her abdomen for about a month. The larvae are pelagic until 7–8 mm long. These prawns become sexually mature after a year, when *c*. 4 cm long. A considerable proportion of the population dies in particularly cold years. They feed on small worms and crustaceans and are caught in seine or trap nets, the main fishing grounds being off the coasts of the western Baltic Sea.

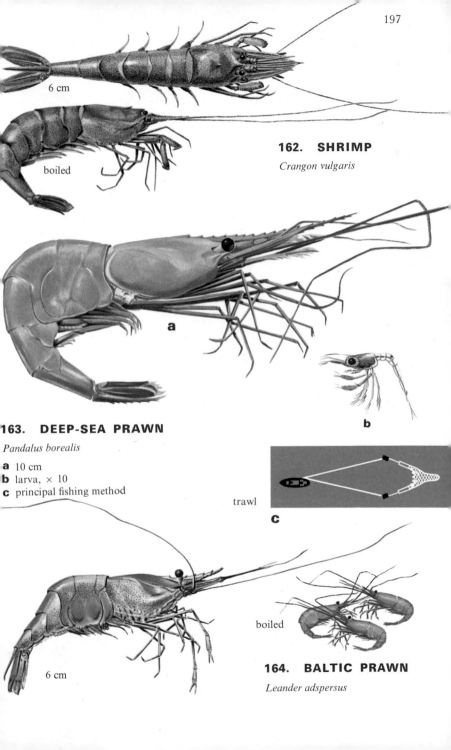

6 cm

boiled

162. SHRIMP
Crangon vulgaris

163. DEEP-SEA PRAWN
Pandalus borealis

a 10 cm
b larva, × 10
c principal fishing method

a

b

trawl

c

boiled

6 cm

164. BALTIC PRAWN
Leander adspersus

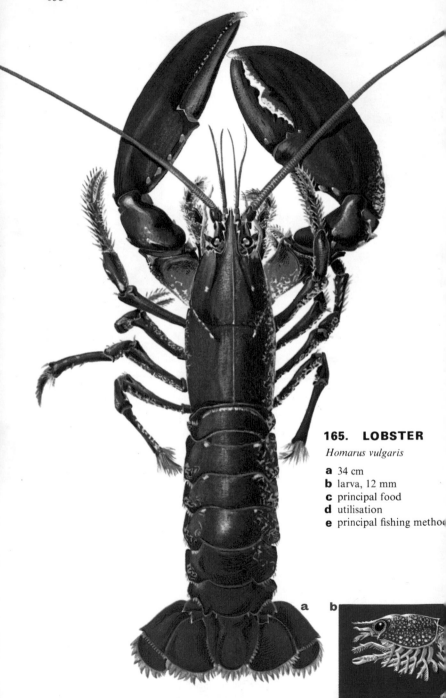

165. LOBSTER

Homarus vulgaris

a 34 cm
b larva, 12 mm
c principal food
d utilisation
e principal fishing method

65. Lobster

Homarus vulgaris Milne Edwards

Maximum length 75 cm (4 kg), but rarely over 30 cm (*c.* 1 kg). Lives in rocky areas with algal growth in depths of 2–40 m. It has rather special temperature requirements: it stops feeding below 5°C and dies at 20–22°C. Breeding only takes place in high salinity water at a temperature of at least 15°C. Mating and the transfer of the sperm packet (spermatophore) takes place in later summer immediately after the female has moulted. The spermatophore is stored over the winter in the female's sperm receptacle and it is not until the following summer that the eggs are fertilised and laid. The female lies on her back and attaches the eggs to the swimmer-ts on the underside of her abdomen. The number of eggs produced varies from 5,000–40,000 according to the size of the female. They take 10–12 months to hatch, depending on the temperature. The larvae (length 7–8 mm) are free-swimming for *c.* 14 days, and after they have moulted three times they move down to the bottom. The lobster is a typical nocturnal animal, which feeds on bivalves, worms, dead fish and weaker members of its own species. It does not undertake long migrations and tagged specimens have been found to have moved 4–5 km at the most. Growth is slow and varies somewhat according to the water temperature. In the Skagerrak the males become sexually mature at a length of 16–17 cm, the females at 22–23 cm (*c.* 350 g, age 5–7 years). The adults moult once or twice a year, becoming 1–2 cm longer each time they do so.

Lobsters are caught in summer in pots which are baited with fresh or dried fish, and kept alive in submerged cages. The population has become much reduced and in Norway, for example, efforts are being made to rear them artificially.

The annual European catch is 2,000 tons, of which Britain takes 1,000 tons, Ireland and France each 300 tons, Norway 200 tons, Sweden 100 tons, Spain 50 tons.

In order to conserve the remaining stocks most of the countries that fish for lobsters have introduced protection measures and also a minimum permissible length (usually 20–21 cm).

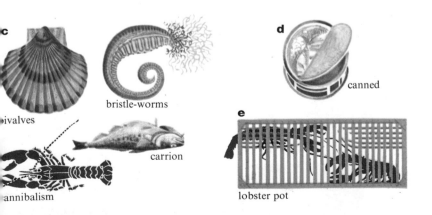

bivalves

bristle-worms

carrion

cannibalism

canned

lobster pot

a

b

c

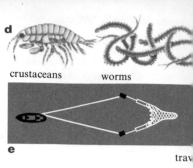

d crustaceans   worms

e   traw

166.   DUBLIN BAY PRAWN

Nephrops norvegicus (L.)

a 18 cm
b egg
c larva, 7 mm
d principal food
e principal fishing method

Also known as the Norway lobster.

From the rostral spine (between the eyes
to the end of the abdomen the male
measure 24 cm at the most, the female
20 cm, but they are rarely over 15 cm
Dublin Bay prawns live on soft bottoms i
depths of 40–250 m, usually spending th
day buried but coming out at night to lur
for prey. The female spawns every secon
year in the period March-November. Th
eggs (up to 4,000) are fertilised as they ar
laid and are carried around on the under
side of the female's abdomen until the
hatch after about 8–9 months. The larvae
which are *c.* 7 mm long, are free
swimming for 2–3 weeks. After their thir
moult they are 11 mm long and they the
move to the bottom. Growth is very slow.

Dublin Bay prawns feed on worms, crustaceans and other small invertebrates, and they become sexually mature in the 3rd-5th year when 8–10 cm long.

They are caught in trawls and seines. The catch is usually cooked on board and most of it goes to canning factories.

The annual European catch is 30,000–35,000 tons, of which Britain and France take 10,000 tons each, Iceland 4,000 tons, Spain 3,000 tons, Ireland 2,000 tons, Denmark 1,500 tons. Several have a minimum permissible length (11–16 cm).

67. CRAWFISH

Palinurus vulgaris Latreille

a 26 cm
b pelagic larva
c fishing method

Without claws. Average length 30–40 cm, maximum 50 cm. Lives on rocky ground in depths of 50–100 m, or even deeper in winter. The eggs (up to 15,000) are carried by the female on the underside of her abdomen during the winter. They hatch in spring into the peculiarly shaped larvae (length 3 mm) which live a pelagic life for *c*. 2 months, until they are *c*. 20 mm long.

Crawfish (or marine crayfish) feed mainly on molluscs. They are caught in pots or other traps and are marketed fresh, frozen or canned. France 600 tons, Spain and Portugal 300 tons, Britain and Ireland 100 tons each.

a

b c

crawfish pot

Breton crawfish boat

18 cm

168.　SPIDER-CRAB

Maia squinado (Herbst)

Average breadth of carapace 8–11 cm, maximum 18 cm. Widely distributed from the English Channel to the Mediterranean, mostly on sandy grounds. In July the sexually mature individuals come together in large aggregations (up to 80 have been observed in one place). The sperm are transferred immediately after the females have moulted. The freshly moulted defenceless females stay in the innermost part of the aggregation. The eggs are laid 6 months later and carried by the females for *c.* 9 months until they hatch into larvae.

Spider-crabs feed on bryozoans and hydroids. They are of some economic importance.

169.　Edible crab

Cancer pagurus L.

Carapace seldom over 20 cm in breadth, maximum 30 cm (4–6 kg). Abdomen broad and rounded in the female, narrow and pointed in the male. Edible crabs live a stationary life on sandy or stony ground, in depths of 1–30 m in summer, 30–50 m in winter. Mating takes place immediately after the females have moulted; the sperms can be stored for a long time (2–3 years) within the body of the female. The female lays $\frac{1}{2}$–3 million eggs in autumn and carries them on her abdomen during the winter. The eggs hatch in the following summer into pelagic larvae that are 0·9 mm long. In the course of two months and after several moults these reach a length of 4 mm, and then move down to live on the bottom. At the end of their first year the young crabs are *c.* 3 cm long. They become sexually mature when 5–6 years old, with a carapace about 12 cm across. Older individuals only moult once a year. They feed on bivalve molluscs and various other bottom-living animals.

Edible crabs are caught in lobster pots baited with fresh fish. They are marketed fresh or frozen, and some of the catch is canned. A crab 10 cm across yields *c.* 100 g of crab meat. Protection measures and minimum sizes have been introduced in several countries. Annual yields are: Britain 5,000–6,000 tons, Norway 3,000 tons.

169. EDIBLE CRAB

Cancer pagurus

a 17 cm
b pelagic larva, × 6
c bottom stage, × 6

a

b

c

204

170.   Northern squid

Loligo forbesi Steenstrup

Body length (without head and arms) seldom over 35 cm for the females and 60 cm for the males. Pelagic animals in coastal waters. During autumn there are large shoals in the northern North Sea. The eggs are laid on the bottom in long, gelatinous club-shaped capsules. Young squids feed on planktonic animals, the older ones hunt small herring, sprats and sand-eels. Like other cephalopods they have venom glands which release a secretion when the powerful jaws seize something, and this paralyses or kills the prey. They live for 2–5 years.

Squids are commonly caught in the trawl and about 200 tons are taken annually in the North Sea; this catch is frozen or canned for export to southern Europe.

There are about 40 species of ten-armed

cephalopods in the North Sea. Although closely related to the snails and bivalves, being molluscs, they are much more like fishes in their habits. Many of them occur in dense shoals and also undertake extensive seasonal migrations, lay free-floating eggs and live a predatory oceanic life hunting shoaling fishes, while they themselves are preyed upon by tunny and whales. The smallest species are *c.* 3 cm long, the largest reach a body length of 2–4 m, with arms up to 10 m long. A squid eye with a diameter of 40 cm has been found in the stomach of a sperm whale.

In warmer seas the fishery for ten-armed (decapod) and eight-armed (octopod) cephalopods is of great economic importance. The annual world catch is *c.* 1 million tons, of which 20,000–30,000 tons are landed in the Mediterranean.

171.   Lesser octopus

Eledone cirrhosa Lamarck

With only a single row of suckers along each arm. Reaches a length of 50 cm at the most, and in the North Sea is found in depths of 5–200 m. In the period July–October the females lay *c.* 800 oval stalked eggs (8 × 3 mm) in large bunches between stones and in rock crevices. These hatch into larvae which are free-swimming for about one month. The adults feed mainly on crabs and bivalve molluscs and are themselves hunted by cod and conger eels. Of no economic importance.

The common octopus (*Octopus vulgaris*) occurs from the Channel coasts to the Mediterranean; it has two rows of suckers along each arm and reaches a length of up to 1 m (2–3 kg). It may locally cause considerable damage to the fisheries by stealing lobsters and crawfish from traps.

Most eight-armed cephalopods live on the bottom in coastal waters, remaining hidden by day in caves and crevices.

Lesser octopus

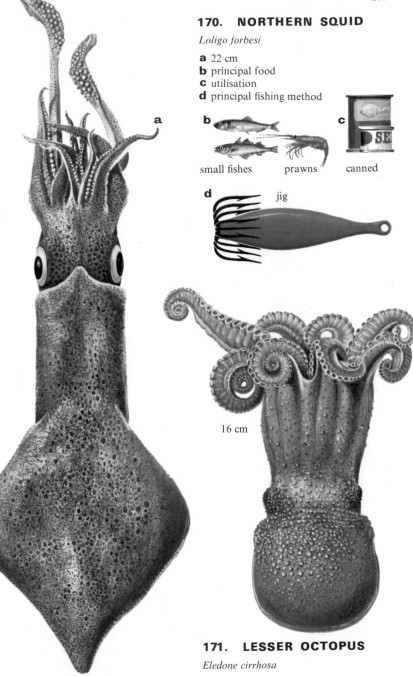

170. NORTHERN SQUID

Loligo forbesi

a 22 cm
b principal food
c utilisation
d principal fishing method

a

b small fishes   prawns   **c** canned

d jig

16 cm

171. LESSER OCTOPUS

Eledone cirrhosa

172. Oyster

Ostrea edulis L.

Lives on firm ground in shallow coastal waters down to depths of *c.* 20 m. The biology of oysters is very interesting. Throughout their whole life they change sex, according to the temperature and feeding conditions. When 8–10 months old, at a temperature of at least 12°C, they first mature into males. Later on, at summer temperatures of 15–16°C, they become females in every 3rd-4th year (every year at 20–22°C) and only function as males in the intervening periods. The sperm are released in the summer. The eggs are fertilised in the gill cavity of the female and remain there until, after 1–2 weeks, they hatch into larvae. These are free-swimming in the plankton for 10–20 days and they then attach themselves to rocks, seaweeds or harbour works by the left shell. With increasing age the shell valves become irregular and wavy. When the valves are cut apart one sees the powerful adductor muscle, surrounded by the heart, stomach, liver, intestine, gonads, all encircled by the four dark gills (the beard).

Oysters feed on plankton, which they filter out of the sea water with the help of the gill filtration apparatus. Maximum age 20–30 years. Ready for market in the 3rd-4th year. To ensure a regular supply oysters are bred and reared in special oyster beds.

Most of the French oysters come from the Arcachon area on the Atlantic coast. The Portuguese oyster, *Crassostrea angulata*, is fished from Brittany to the Mediterranean; it differs in having *violet* marks where the adductor muscle is attached to the inside of each shell.

173. Mussel

Mytilus edulis L.

Seldom over 80 mm in length. Lives in the intertidal zone in depths of 0–10 m, frequently in places with a strong swell. The sexes are separate and the eggs and sperm are released into the surrounding water. A single female produces 5–12 million eggs which are then fertilised. They hatch in about 1–2 weeks into very tiny larvae which are free-swimming for 2–3 weeks and then settle on rocks, seaweed etc. They become attached to substrates of this type by threads secreted by the byssus gland.

Like the oyster, the mussel is also bred and cultivated in suitable places. They reach marketable size in 1–4 years, according to the amount of available food and are sold fresh or canned. Some of the yield is processed into fish meal.

During recent years the fishery for mussels has been seriously damaged by a parasitic copepod (*Mytilicola intestinalis*). This parasite lives in the mussel's gut where it may cause abnormal growth. The flesh of infected mussels is not however, injurious. Holland 80,000–100,000 tons. Spain 100,000 tons, France 30,000 tons, Denmark 20,000–30,000 tons, Germany 6,000–100,000 tons.

172. OYSTER

Ostrea edulis

a 7 cm
b pelagic larva, 0·24 mm
c principal fishing method

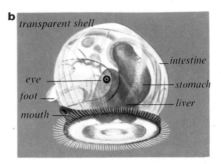

Roofing tiles, stakes and brushwood are used as spat collectors, on which the young oysters settle.

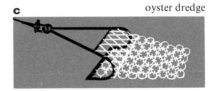

173. MUSSEL

Mytilus edulis

5–7 cm

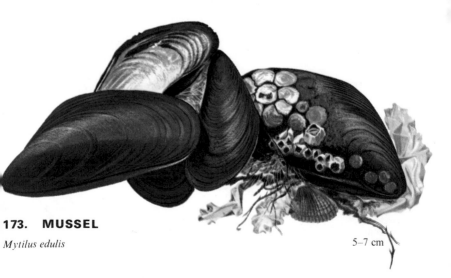

HISTORY
OF THE
FISHERIES

Figurehead from steamship Finnmark, year 1864.
Bergen Museum.

Ancient times

There is no doubt that fishing is one of man's earliest activities designed to provide a food supply. The beginnings of sea fisheries in their simplest form can, in fact, be followed along the coasts of Europe from the early Stone Age onwards.

At first fisheries involved merely the collecting activities of prehistoric man. Whereas in inland areas he mainly collected insects, frogs, root and fruits, his congeners along the coast were able to gather crabs, mussels and small fishes when the tide was low. Soon they built artificial barriers, such as stone walls and traps, which held back the treasures of the sea as the tide flowed out. In early times man also began to catch fish in inland lakes and rivers and along the shore by using the traditional hunting gear: bows and arrows, and spears.

Thus, fishing became an interesting occupation for the men, while the more tedious collecting was left to the women and children. As we know from cave paintings magic played an important role.

Halibut, rock-engraving from Stavanger, Norway.

The forerunner of the fish hook was a pointed spindle-shaped toggle, similar to those still used by primitive peoples. Although hooks were a later invention than the arrow and spear, they were known in their present form in the Stone Age; they were carved out of stone, horn, bone or wood, but they were not known in all parts of the world. They were first introduced into Australia and large areas of Africa by the Europeans and Arabs. By the Bronze Age and early Ice Age the fish hook had already reached the typical form we know today.

Quite early on man started to make traps out of interwoven twigs or canes, a technique which is still used (eel baskets, lobster pots). In rivers and small bays he constructed fish barriers which led the fish into specially designed traps.

In inland areas nets were used for catching birds and man soon learned to adapt these for catching fish, by dragging them through the water or casting them.

The captured fishes were split open and either dried in the sun or smoked over a fire to provide reserve supplies of food.

In the Bronze and early Iron Ages boat-building made great progress. At first there were boats with stretched skins, rafts and hollowed tree trunks and then sailing boats with clinker-built cladding. Fishing was originally aimed at providing a means of subsistence, but as catches increased trading in fishery products started to flourish.

Men learned about the preserving power of salt. Even some 3,000 years ago salt and salted fish were important articles of commerce in the Mediterranean. The Phoenicians, in particular, had a very prosperous trade in salt fish, and the names of

tunny with necklace on an Ionian coin, c. 600 B.C.

many towns bear witness to this. Thus, Sidon means 'the fisherman's town' and Malaga is 'the place where the fish were salted'. It was, however, more than 1,000 years before knowledge of the preserving properties of salt penetrated to the countries of northern Europe.

Middle Ages

During the Middle Ages it was still not possible to transport fresh fish over long distances. Fish could only be marketed where it was landed and in towns near the coast, and those who lived inland had to rely on inland fisheries which played a more important role than they do at the present day.

From the economic viewpoint the most important fish were herring and cod, just as they are today. Salt became an extremely important raw material. Along the coasts, sea water was led into shallow lagoons (salt pans) where sun and wind helped to evaporate it. In northern Europe salt was produced by boiling sea water in large salt pans heated by burning wood or charcoal. Many forests in England, Holland and Denmark were destroyed for the sake of salt production.

hooks made of stone and bone

bast netting from the Stone Age

Yarmouth.
England

Enkhuizen,
Holland

Skagen,
Denmark

Marstrand,
Sweden

Bergen, Norway,
a Hanseatic
town

Fisheries were so important to some towns that they incorporated fish in their coat of arms.

Towards the end of the Middle Ages salt was heavily taxed, as tobacco is today. This led to smuggling which was combatted by numerous laws and regulations.

The herring fishery began to develop as early as the year 1000 along the coast of eastern England. Yarmouth was even then an important fishing port. At the same time fishing also took place in the English Channel and in the southern North Sea off Dieppe, Calais and the Netherlands.

From the 13th century on the most important centre for the supply of salt herring to Europe was in the area of the southern Öresund; the main places involved were Falsterbo and Skanör. The sale of these herrings was in the hands of the north German Hanseatic towns which bought extensive privileges from the Danish king and controlled the export for over 400 years. Around 1500 the Flemish herring began to compete on the market, and the monopoly position of the Hanseatic League was gradually broken. However, even in the year 1537 some 37,500 men were employed at Skanör and Falsterbo in salting 96,000 barrels of herring. In addition, a further 264,000 barrels came from other fishing grounds in the Danish kingdom.

Danish herring were originally salted uncleaned, but later they were carefully gutted and washed so that the quality and keeping power were improved. The Dutchmen learned this method of preparation from the Hanseatic merchants around the year 1375 and improved it in the course of time.

The uniform high quality was insured by numerous laws and regulations on processing and subsequent treatment. As a result Flemish herring gradually took over first place in the market from the Hanseatic League, a position which it maintained for c. 300 years. The herring trade laid the foundations for the wealth of Holland and enabled this small country at the end of the 16th century to finance its war of independence against the might of Spain.

Dutch fisheries used special three-masted vessels of 80–100 tons, the herring busses, which had a crew of 14–15 men. Trawling was the most important fishing method. At the beginning of the herring season fast-sailing boats brought the first expensive herring to Holland, whence it was transported further afield by light horse-drawn carts.

At that period there were about 2,000 Dutch herring busses fishing in the North Sea, and they were frequently guarded against privateers and pirates by armed vessels. It has been estimated that at that time about a fifth of the Dutch population (i.e. *c.* 450,000 men) derived their income directly or indirectly from the herring fishery. This accounts for the saying, still current, that Amsterdam is built on herring bones.

Since the early Middle Ages cod (sometimes split) that has been dried by wind and sun has been a very important source of food in the Scandinavian countries. It provided a suitable supply for carrying on board ship, and thus enabled fishermen to undertake the long voyage to Iceland and Greenland.

During the 13th and 14th centuries the Hanseatic merchants began to build up their export trade from Bergen, using the native products: stockfish and fish oil. The English from Bristol started similar trading with Iceland, and also fished Icelandic coastal waters with their two-masted vessels, "Doggers".

Liver oil was an important by-product of the cod fishery. The oil was mainly used in the preparation and care of leather, and also as a very evil-smelling, smut-producing lamp oil. It was not until 1775 that the use of cod liver oil as a preventive against rickets was discovered in England. Subsequently it was, of course, found to have a high content of vitamins A and D and its use is now widespread.

Modern times

'On 10th August 1497. For the discoverer of the new island, £10'.

This was the amount entered in his private cash book by the King of England as a gift to John Cabot for discovering

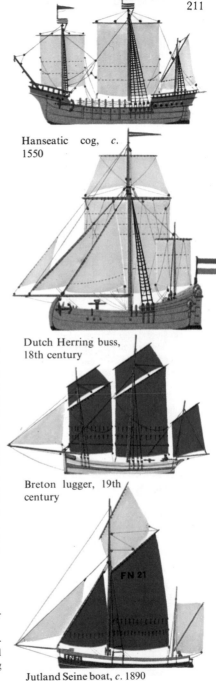

Hanseatic cog, *c.* 1550

Dutch Herring buss, 18th century

Breton lugger, 19th century

Jutland Seine boat, *c.* 1890

beam trawl; English drawing 1635

Newfoundland. It was, however, several years before the enormous value of this island to English fisheries was fully realised.

During the first half of the 16th century the waters around Newfoundland were mainly fished by Spanish, Portuguese and French fishermen. When, however, Denmark started to impose an expensive licensing system on English fishermen operating off Iceland, there came a time when England began to send fishing boats to Newfoundland in large numbers. Around 1580 there were 50 English, 50 Portuguese, 100 Spanish and 150 French boats fishing off Newfoundland, but after English pirates had driven off the Spanish and Portuguese, England and France took over the sole control of the fisheries in this area. In 1583 the English colonised the island and forced the French to fish further away from its coasts, and this resulted in the French discovering the very profitable fishing on the Newfoundland Banks. England took over the extensive trade in salted cod with Spain and Portugal. The English fishing fleet would sail in spring to

trading in dried salt fish. Olaus Magnus 1555

Portugal to pick up salt, move on to Newfoundland to catch cod and then sail back to Portugal to deliver the salt fish. On their voyage back to England they carried wine, olive oil and salt. While the English controlled the market for fish in the Iberian Peninsula, the Dutch moved into the waters along the east coast of England and sold vast quantities of fish on the English market.

By 1630 the total tonnage of the English Newfoundland fleet had risen to 27,000 tons, and the annual proceeds of the fishery amounted to c. £180,000. The French made two fishing trips a year to Newfoundland, where they used long lines. The catch was salted on board and packed in barrels. The French vessels had a crew of 15–20 men and carried supplies for 6 months. By the beginning of the 18th century the French were outstripping the English; they had 4,000–8,000 fishing boats and 16,000–30,000 men employed, whereas England had only 5,000 men engaged in the Newfoundland fishery.

During the 18th century the French were using fishing schooners of 200–300 tons with a crew of 70–80 men and 14–15 dories; the latter are small boats from which the men fished with long lines.

The economic position of New England was much improved by the Newfoundland fishery and in quite a short time Boston, in particular, developed into an important fishing port.

The well-organised Dutch herring fishery in the North Sea had a long period of prosperity, and all the attempts of the English to establish a similarly valuable system failed. It was not until the numerous wars between England and France during the 17th and 18th century that the Dutch monopoly was broken. The Scottish and English herring fishery, with government bounties and financial aid for building boats, was now able to develop rapidly. The British herring catch reached its peak in 1913 with c. 600,000 tons, most of which was exported to Russia, Poland and Germany.

In more recent times the yield of the
herring fishery has fluctuated considerably;
good herring years off south-west Norway
have alternated with good periods off the
Swedish Kattegat coast. The Norwegian
herring periods lasted *c.* 50–80, the Swedish
40–60 years. Of greater economic importance for the west Norwegian fishery is the
Atlanto-Scandinavian herring which first
appeared on the European market as salt
herring in the 18th century, after Holland
had lost its premier position in the herring
trade.

Fish of the cod group were first processed
into klipfisk in the Nordic countries about
the beginning of the 17th century. This
product, together with stockfish, quickly
became an important export. By 1827 some
30,000 men were working in the Lofoten
fishery, which is still one of the largest in
Europe. Klipfisk and stockfish are mainly
exported to Spain, Portugal, Italy and
South America.

During the Napoleonic Wars it became
necessary to preserve food, in order to
provide the vast numbers of men with
transportable food. The first attempts to
preserve food in glass containers were made
towards the end of the 18th century. The
first patent for preserved food in tin cans
was issued in 1810, and 15 years later one

Herring fishery   Olaus Magnus 1535

could buy salmon, sardines and crab in
cans.

The trade in fresh fish could make no real
progress until methods were developed for
keeping it fresh for a period of time in
crushed ice. Natural ice was collected in
winter from inland lakes or imported from
Norway and stored for several months in
well-insulated cellars. The first ice-making
machine was invented in 1835, and by 1890
all the main sea-fishing ports had their own
ice factory. With the development of the
railway systems it became possible rapidly
to transport fresh, iced fish on special fish
trains to inland towns. The highly salted,
dried or smoked products of former times
were no longer in demand, and were
replaced by fresh or mildly smoked
products.

In principle, the actual fishing gear has
changed little since the Middle Ages.
Practically all the present-day fishing
methods were in use then, and the only
changes have been improvements in the
gear and an increase in its size. The
discovery of the steam engine provided the
greatest impetus to fisheries, as it did to
industry in general.

After 1880 the first British steam trawlers
were in operation, and soon after this there
were also steam drifters. The old beam
trawl was now replaced by the otter trawl
which is much easier to manoeuvre.
Machinery was also used for winding up
the anchor and the nets.

The development of electricity was also
of great importance to the fisheries. Even
before the First War trawlers were being
fitted with wireless. Nowadays, all deep-sea
trawlers are equipped with wireless tele-
graphy and echo-sounding equipment.

As the North Sea began to show clear
signs of overfishing and the demand for
fish has constantly grown it has become
necessary during the present century to find
new productive fishing grounds. Suitable
large populations have mainly been found
in the Arctic, and the Barents Sea,
Denmark Strait and the waters off west
Greenland have become important fishing
areas. Formerly the smaller steam trawlers
fished in depths of 20–200 m, but now the
populations in deeper water can also be

exploited. In so doing some bottom-living fishes, such as redfish, that were previously unknown on the market are now landed in large amounts (*c.* 500,000 tons of redfish), whereas around the turn of the century such species were of no importance as human food, and if caught in large quantities were often thrown overboard.

Nowadays the modern trawlers work together with factory ships which take the fish on board for processing; they are equipped with refrigeration and with machines for filleting and for making fish meal. These ships also carry workshops, sick-bays, food stores and accommodation for reserve crews. This method of fishing is practised particularly by the Soviet Union and Japan. The increase in equipment has necessitated the construction of large and technically complicated fishing ports with gigantic unloading and dispatch facilities.

The smaller forms of coastal fishing have not changed very radically. Nowadays small decked motor vessels are used, as well as sailing boats and open rowing boats. The most serious problem is the shortage of crews; just as there is a drift of country people into the towns, so many young men move from coastal fishing to the better paid, industrialised deep-sea fishery.

Aberdeen's first steam trawler 1882.

ISHING TECHNIQUES

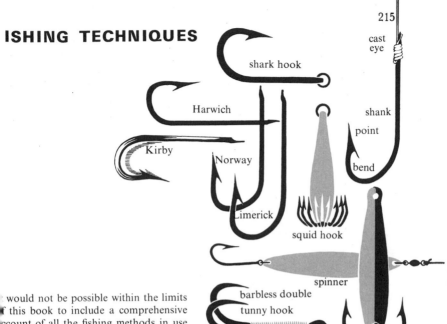

shark hook

Harwich

Kirby

Norway

Limerick

squid hook

cast eye

shank

point

bend

spinner

barbless double
tunny hook

jig

would not be possible within the limits
f this book to include a comprehensive
ccount of all the fishing methods in use
day. Many techniques are, however, only
f subordinate importance to the fisheries
.g. fish spears and harpoons which are
sed for hunting individual fish) and these
ill not be discussed. In the following
ction only the most important methods
ill be described in some detail.

ook and line

he fishing hook is one of the oldest of
an's tools, and is still used in all parts of
e world; it has been estimated that there
e about 30,000 different types. In
rthern and western Europe the demand
r hooks is satisfied mainly by British and
orwegian firms; the hooks are made of
eel, more rarely of brass, and often
lvanized to prevent rusting.

A hook consists of an eye, a shank, a
nd and a point. The eye is either in the
rm of a small flattened area or has a ring
r fastening on the cast. The point is
ually barbed, but there may be no barb
in the hooks used in commercial tunny
hing.

The most important hook types are the
Norway, Harwich, Limerick and Kirby
of which the majority are made in 24
different sizes, the smallest hook having
the highest number. Thus for cod fishing
one can use a Norway No. 8, but for
halibut a Norway No. 3. Unfortunately,
the numbering is not uniform for all types
of hook. The main difference between the
different types is in the shape of the bend.

A jig consists of two or more hooks embedded in or fixed to a small metal 'fish'.
The jig is not baited but is moved up and
down by jerking to attract the fish.

Spinning baits (e.g. spoons) are artificial
bait 'fish' which are thrown out and pulled
in so that they twist and turn in the water.

The cast is the connecting piece between
the fishing line and the hook and it may be
made of catgut, nylon, silk or, for shark
fishing, steel wire.

There are several different methods of fishing with hooks (legering, paternosters, trolling, fishing with a rod, etc). In simple hand fishing with a lead weight, jig,

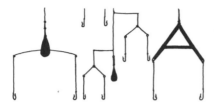

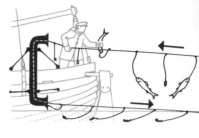

spinner or baited hook the fish is lured by moving the line up and down. The line may have several side lines with hooks (paternosters). The old methods of fishing by hand are not much used nowadays, and sports fishermen use fishing rods of different types.

In trolling one uses natural or artificial spinning baits attached to a long line which is towed behind a boat. There may be two lines, kept apart by otter boards and also weighted. The modern method of catching

mackerel on the principle of a 'moving band' is shown diagrammatically above.

Long lines are particularly important to the fisheries. These are very long lengths (50–150 fathoms) of fishing line with short branch lines (snoods) carrying the hooks at set intervals. These are baited on land or on the way out to the fishing grounds. Several of these lines may be joined together to give a total length of several kilometres. The position of the line and hooks in the water can be adjusted according to the type of fish that one intends to catch (e.g. near the bottom, or floating in mid-water; see figure). Long lines are mainly used in places where the bottom conditions do not permit the use of a trawl.

Long lines are employed especially for catching sharks, salmon, eels, garfish, cod, redfish, halibut and Greenland halibut.

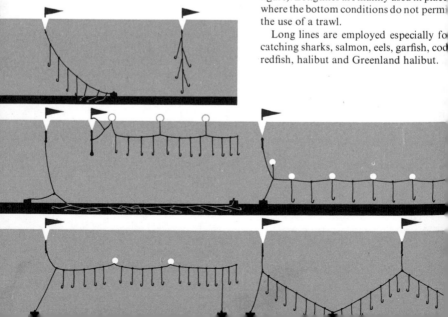

The baits used include herring, sand-eels, apelin, gobies, cottids, prawns, crabs, ussels, squids etc. The bait is either ept alive in tanks or stored in frozen r slightly salted conditions. Artificial baits pieces of coloured plastic, rubber rings, tc) are also used in hand fishing and olling.

Long lines are often used on the fishing anks. The large factory ships carry a umber of rowing boats (dories). These sh by day in the vicinity of the larger essel to which they deliver their catch in ne evening. The fish are salted and stored n the factory ship (a single trip may last –5 months). This type of fishery is mainly ractised by Portuguese schooners; a large actory ship of 700 tons may be equipped ith 50 dories, which are stored on board ne above the other, and which often use ails in order to save space required for uel storage.

Nets

Fishing nets may be made of hemp, otton, nylon or other synthetic fibres. Along the upper edge of the net there is a ead rope which has floats of cork, foam lastic or hollow spheres of glass, metal r plastic, while the foot rope along the ower edge carries weights of lead, stone or on chain.

The length of the net is measured in athoms (1 fathom = 1·88 m), and its depth y the number of meshes. The mesh size is iven as the distance from one knot to the

next or as the length of a single mesh, when fully stretched. To prevent rotting, the netting is tanned or impregnated. For this the mesh may be tanned in a hot decoction of the bark of oak, birch, pine,

different netting knots

quebracho, catechu, etc, dried, dipped in a copper compound (copper sulphate, etc), and then carefully washed. Tar and tar products are also used. The nets shrink somewhat in the water, particularly those with a small mesh; attention must be paid to this when nets with different mesh sizes are being made. The nets are dried by hanging them up in the shade, to avoid the injurious effect of bright sunshine.

Drift nets and set nets

Drift nets hang vertically like curtains in the open water. They are set out in the open sea to catch pelagic fishes, such as herring, mackerel, saithe and salmon. Usually several nets are joined together to form a 'fleet' which may be up to a kilometre long. Different types of floats and weights are used to keep the net at the surface or at a certain depth. Drift nets function as gill nets, the fish swimming into them, becoming entangled and caught.

A set gill net is put out along the sea floor to catch bottom-living fishes, (such as cod and flatfishes). Usually several nets are put out in a long row. One special type, the trammel net, consists of a loosely set fine-meshed net (inner net) and one or two

ead rope ith floats

oot rope ith weights

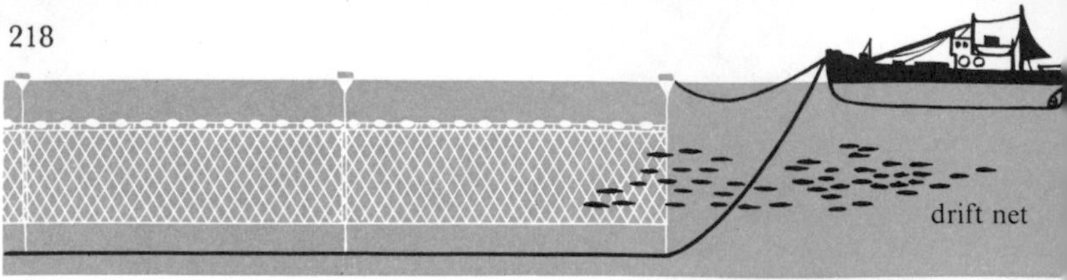

drift net

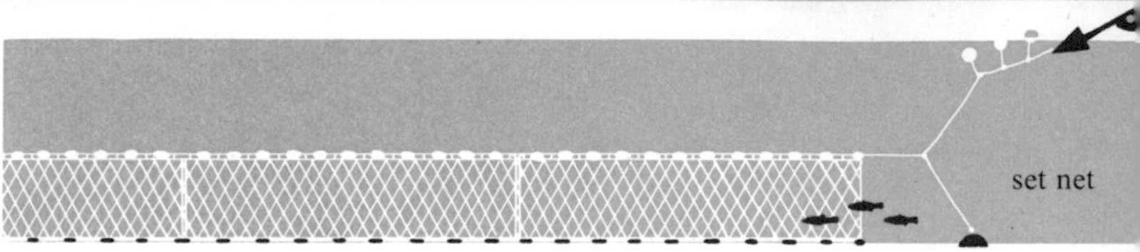

set net

wide-meshed outer nets. When a fish swims up against such a net it draws the mesh of the inner net through one of the meshes of the outer net and becomes caught in the resulting pocket of netting. This efficient net, even if somewhat heavy to

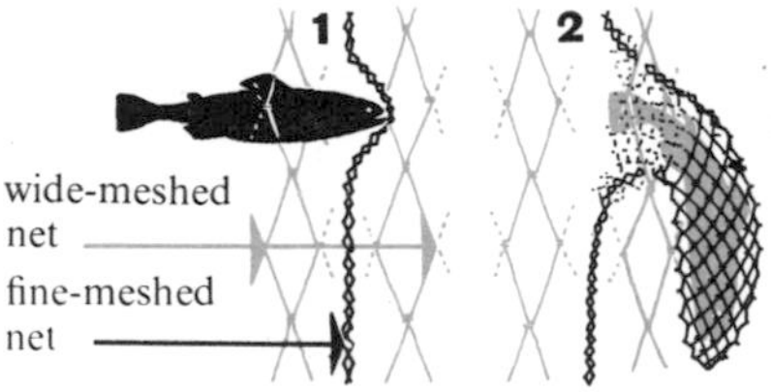

wide-meshed net

fine-meshed net

handle, is frequently used in coastal fisheries to catch salmon and flatfishes.

In places where the bottom is too ha for posts to be driven in, large floati traps anchored to buoys are used. This ty of gear is used in Norway and Sweden f catching salmon.

Fixed nets are used particularly in coast fisheries for the capture of herring, salmo eels, cod, garfish, and also for macke when these come inshore on their annu breeding and feeding migrations.

Tonnaras are enormous bottom ne used for catching tunny. The leader net up to 3–4 kilometres long and it leads t fish into a series of chambers. The fin chamber has a bottom or floor of nettin and it can be hauled up. Tonnaras a similar installations are mostly set up narrow channels and bays. The large

Fixed nets

These are special large traps that are firmly anchored on the bottom in shallow water and they are used for catching herring, mackerel and eels. A long leader net guides the fish to a funnel-shaped entrance which opens into a chamber, which has side walls reaching to the water surface and is closed at the bottom by netting. The netting walls are supported by posts or by ropes suspended from posts.

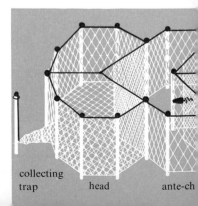

collecting trap   head   ante-ch

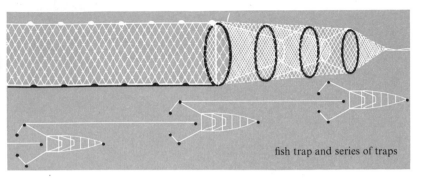

fish trap and series of traps

catch is taken by Spain in the Straits of Gibraltar.

Traps

Braced traps consist of bags of netting which are kept open by rings or hoops of cane, osier or iron. A leader net guides the fish into the capture chamber which usually has short wings or an antechamber to prevent the fish escaping at the sides. The entrance to the trap is funnel-shaped; this allows the fish to enter, but prevents them moving back. It is usual to operate several such traps arranged in series.

Traps are used in shallow water for the capture of eels, cod, prawns, etc.

Basket traps are barrel-shaped structures made out of osiers, with one or two funnel-shaped openings. A bait is placed inside the trap which is then put out in a suitable position on the sea bottom.

Such traps are used for catching eels, conger eels, lobsters, crawfish, edible crabs and cuttlefishes. In Europe thousands of tons are caught annually in eel baskets.

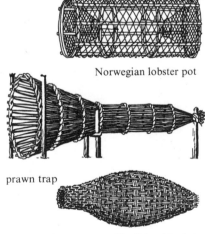

Norwegian lobster pot

prawn trap

English eel basket

Purse seines

Seine nets are among the most important of all kinds of fishing gear, particularly

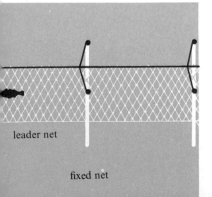

leader net

fixed net

for catching pelagic fishes in large numbers, e.g. herring. These nets may be over 200 fathoms long and 30–45 fathoms deep; they are constructed of netting of different mesh sizes and yarn strengths. The smallest mesh and the strongest yarn are in the centre part of the net in which the fish congregate before it is hauled in. The upper edge of the net is kept at the surface by floats (cork, canvas bladders). The lower edge hangs down in the water and in addition to a number of weights it has a series of bronze or brass rings through which a purse line runs.

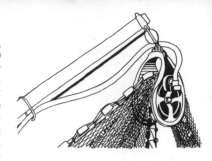

This gear is shot in a circle round a fish shoal, usually by two boats moving against the wind. After the fish have been encircled the purse line is tightened, thus closing the net at the bottom. The catch can then be hauled in. When the catch has been concentrated in the middle part of the net it is either scooped on board with nets or, when a mother ship is used, heaved up in baskets which take 10–20 hectolitres at a time.

In recent years the efficiency of seine nets has been greatly increased by the use of the Puretic power block for winding the net in; with this gear it is not longer necessary to have the two small boats for shooting the net.

Seine nets are used for catching pilchards, anchovies, herring, sprat, mackerel, tunny, scad, capelin, cod and saithe.

Electric or acetylene lamps are often used when fishing at night. The fish gather

into a dense swarm beneath the light and can then be surrounded by the net. This method is much used in the Mediterranean.

There is a variant of such nets, which instead of the purse line has a sac-like bulge in the middle where the fish congregate.

Beach seines are shot in a semicircle and hauled in from the shore. They are mainly used in shallow water

In Norway and Iceland long barrier nets are used to cut off herring shoals in fjords and bays. The net can be hauled up on land for emptying.

Trawl

The trawl is a funnel-shaped sac of netting consisting of two pieces, the upper and the lower nets, joined together at the sides. The upper net extends over the lower net like a

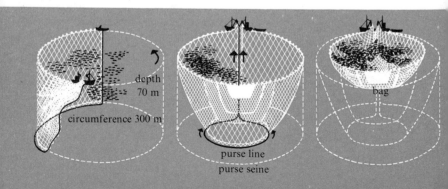

depth 70 m

circumference 300 m

bag

purse line
purse seine

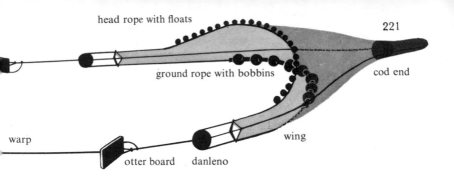

head rope with floats

ground rope with bobbins

cod end

warp

otter board   danleno

wing

roof. The long wings prevent the fish from escaping to the sides. The net gradually narrows to the rear and ends in a long, fine-mesh pouch, known as the cod end in which the fish collect. Sometimes the cod end has a funnel which stops the fish from swimming back.

The net is hauled by two warps. Small trawls may be held open by a transverse bar of wood; this type, known as a beam trawl, is used for example for catching soles. On the other hand, in large trawls the wings are kept apart by otter boards, and this considerably increases the bottom area swept by the trawl. The otter boards are large, flat structures, 2–5 inches thick and made of wood, metal or a combination of both. They are either attached directly to the forward end of each wing or at a distance in front of them. The warps are attached in such a way that these boards sheer outwards when the trawl is towed, thus keeping the net open.

Large steel structures known as danlenos prevent the wings from becoming caught up on small obstacles.

The net opening is kept open by 20–30 (or up to 100) glass or metal floats which are attached to the head rope. In addition, the head rope (or a subsidiary head rope) may have a number of small, obliquely set boards which pull it upwards, thus increasing the vertical dimensions of the trawl mouth. The ground rope, fixed to the lower edge of the net is a steel warp, 2–3 inches in diameter, bound round with manila. When fishing on hard ground the ground rope is fitted with wooden or steel rollers (bobbins), which enable the net to roll over obstacles.

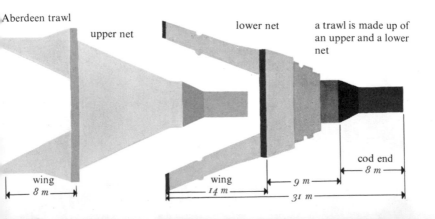

Aberdeen trawl

upper net

lower net

a trawl is made up of an upper and a lower net

wing
8 m

wing
14 m

cod end
8 m

9 m

31 m

For taking flatfishes the best trawling speed is 2–3 knots. Iron chains, stretched loosely in front of the ground rope, scare the fish up from the bottom and thus drive them into the net. For cod and haddock the trawl is towed at 3–5 knots, and for herring at 3–6 knots.

When hauling the trawl in the warps are wound in over two gallows which are usually on the same side of the ship (nor-

mally the starboard). In large modern stern trawlers the trawl is shot from the stern which has a slip for hauling it in.

Trawlers have large, powerful winches, with drums carrying 500–1,000 fathoms of warp. The length of warp used is normally 3–4 times the depths of the water being fished. A single trawl haul usually takes 3 hours.

In the two-ship method the trawl net (without otter boards) is towed by two ships which keep about 300 m apart.

Mid-water trawls

In recent years a pelagic trawl has bee used for catching herring.

The Danish-built Larsen trawl consis of a conical sac of netting, made up of fo equal parts. This is towed by two trawler using two pairs of warps. The two low warps are weighted with weights of 50 200 kg. A large net of this type has a opening of *c.* 40 m and a length of 55 m The tunnel of the net is cylindrical and th cod end is reinforced with nylon. By mea of a 'splitting strap' in front of the co end the catch, if large, can be split up int a number of portions.

Attempts are also being made to con struct a mid-water net towed by only or ship, in which the netting would be ke open by special paravanes (elevator an depressor devices). This presents certai technical problems and the project is sti really in the development stage.

Danish seine

This type of seine was first constructed b the Danish fisherman Jens Vaever in 184 It consists of a sac of netting with lon wings to which the tow lines are attached The upper edge of the net has floa (hollow glass, plastic or aluminiur

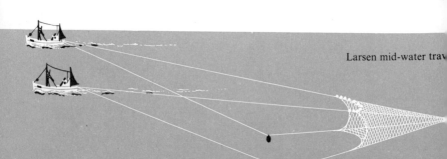

Larsen mid-water traw

distance from ship to trawl, c. 500 m

spheres) and the lower edge has lead weights (20–30 kg).

The net is shot from an anchored buoy to which the end of one tow line is attached. This is then paid out by the boat which sails out from the buoy in a wide curve (1–3 km), until the actual net is reached. The second tow line is paid out on the way back to the anchored buoy. The whole operation may take up to $1\frac{1}{2}$ hours before the boat returns to the buoy, which is then taken on board.

When the gear has been shot the area of catch will have been surrounded and the fishermen now start to wind in the two tow lines. During hauling the lines glide

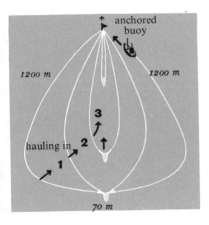

anchored buoy

1200 m   1200 m

3

hauling in **2**

1

70 m

Depending upon the nature of the bottom, the performance of the engine and the expected catch a tow line will be made up of 5–18 coils of rope each c. 120 fathoms long. The rope ends are spliced together as the seine is being shot. The net is usually fished against the current. If the current changes during the day the seine can be shot in a new direction from the same buoy after each haul.

The Danish seine was originally constructed only for catching flatfishes, but since the turn of the century there have been some improvements and it is now also used for taking round fishes, such as cod, haddock, whiting and herring. The Danish seine has the following advantages over the trawl: although it is very efficient and encloses a large fishing area it only requires a boat with a relatively low-powered engine. Furthermore, the catch is of superior quality; the fish only remain a short time in the net and they can be brought alive to the market.

On the other hand, fishing with the Danish seine requires large areas of flat bottom (without obstacles, such as rocks, corals etc). And it can only be used when the speed of the wind and current is low. Danish seine fishing is mainly carried out by small boats with a length of 9–24 m and a crew of 3–4 men. The tow lines are wound in by a winch and automatically shot on to the deck (in coils) by a warp coiling machine which is driven by the winch. This machine was patented by a Danish fisherman in 1903, and has been little altered since then.

slowly over the sea floor and drive the fish in front of them and towards the centre. It is only when the tow lines have come fairly close together that the net itself starts to move and is towed in towards the boat.

The tow lines are made of tough manila rope with a diameter of c. 20 mm.

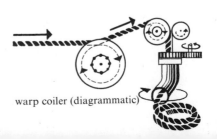

warp coiler (diagrammatic)

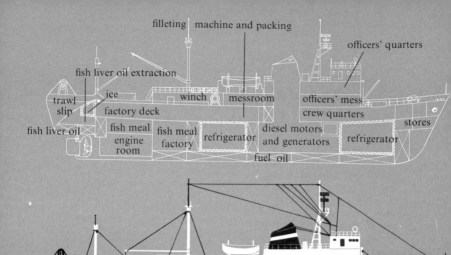

filleting machine and packing

fish liver oil extraction

officers' quarters

trawl slip

ice

winch

messroom

officers' mess

factory deck

crew quarters

fish liver oil

fish meal engine room

fish meal factory

refrigerator

diesel motors and generators

refrigerator

stores

fuel oil

M.T. Fairtry III

Diesel electric stern trawler and factory ship.
2,600 tons. 2,000 H.P., built in England 1959.
Length 82·5 m, breadth 14·5 m.

Refrigeration capacity: 30 tons cod in 24 hrs.
Refrigerator volume: 1,350 cubic metres.
Filleting and packing machines,
fish oil extraction
and fish meal factory.
Crew of 96 men.

officers' quarters

working deck

winch

trawl slip

freezing plant

messroom, crew quarters

crew quarters

stores

fish hold

engine room

refrigerator

fish hold

fuel oil

fish liver oil

M.T. Lord Nelson

English stern trawler. 1,200 tons, 2,000 H.P.,
15 knots. Built in Germany 1961.
Length 71·5 m, breadth 11 m.

Refrigeration capacity: 21 tons fish in 24 hrs.
Refrigerator volume: 329 cubic metres
Fish on ice, 336 cubic metres,
liver oil 40 cubic metres.
Crew of 36 men.

Modern fishing vessels

Modern fishing vessels can be divided into the following main groups:

1 Stern trawler-factory ships. Large vessels for distant water fisheries of 2,800–3,000 tons, a radius of operation of 2,000–4,000 sea miles and trips of 60–80 days. The equipment carried includes filleting machines, packing equipment, fish meal plants, oil extraction and refrigeration. The crew consists of about 100 men, probably working in 3 shifts of 8 hours. The English Fairtry type (see p. 224) will serve as a pattern for the Russian factory ships of the Pushkin and Mayakowsky series and for the Polish B. 15 and B. 18.

2 Mother ships. These factory and supply ships function as mother ships for a fleet of 20–50 smaller trawlers and transport ships. They take the catch on board and provide the fleet with fuel and provisions.

3 Refrigerator ships. Vessels for trawling and line fishing. Their main product is frozen whole fish. This group includes, for example, the modern French tunny clippers (Californian type).

4 Part-freezer trawlers. These are modern trawlers which freeze part of the catch on board. They have a tonnage of 400–1,200, a length of 45–80 metres and a speed of 10–15 knots. With diesel or diesel-electric drive, and 700 to 2,000 H.P. The largest of this type, the long-distance trawlers, undertake fishing trips of c. 24 days. The trawler Lord Nelson, shown on the opposite page, is an example of this type.

The smaller trawlers in this category undertake considerably shorter trips, mostly of about 14 days, and they are now of increasing importance.

5 Coastal and short-distance vessels. These include trawlers of 60–600 tons and a large number of variously constructed cutters and smacks of 20–200 tons. They carry a crew of 4–15 men, and are known under many different names: seine boats, prawn boats, herring drifters, crayfish boats etc.

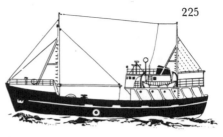

Norwegian vessel for purse seine and line fishing. C. 140 tons, 400 H.P. Length overall 27 m, breadth 6·5 m. Crew of 16 men. With direction-finding equipment, radio-telephone, echo-sounder and Asdic.

French tunny clipper. 125 tons, 150 H.P. Length overall 26 m, breadth 7 m. Four tanks of 10 cubic metres for live bait. Fish storage 80 cubic metres. Crew of 16 men.

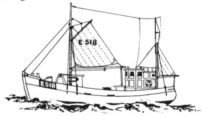

Danish North Sea cutter. 50 tons, 75 H.P. Length overall 20 m, breadth 5 m. Direction-finding equipment, radio telephone, echo-sounder and Decca. Mainly for seine netting, but also for trawling, purse seine and line fishing. Crew of 6 men.

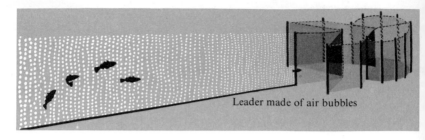

Leader made of air bubbles

New fishing equipment

Attempts are being made in several countries to develop new fishing methods based on the reactions of the fish to light, sound, electric currents etc.

Electric fishing, for example, is based on the fact that fish brought into the vicinity of an electric field will swim to the anode (the positive pole) and congregate there. The Russians have tried to place the anode, together with a powerful electric lamp, at the bottom opening of a suction pipe. The idea is that anchovy or pilchard shoals, attracted by the light, would come into the field of the anode and would then be pumped directly on board the fishing vessel. The pupose of the experiments was to render nets unnecessary as a means of catching fish or else to increase their efficiency with the help of some similar type of equipment. There are, however, many technical difficulties to be overcome before this method can become practical.

Other interesting experiments have been aimed at replacing expensive leader nets and barrier nets by 'curtains' of air bubbles produced from a perforated plastic pipe laid along the bottom. Observations have shown that many fishes will not swim through such a curtain.

Knowledge gained from research on the fish's sense of smell and taste will doubtless also be of great practical importance to the fisheries.

Fish location

For an efficient open ocean fishery it is quite essential that the fisherman should be able to locate fish shoals and to determine their exact depth and extent. It is in this field that the electrical industry has brought to the market excellent equipment which has now become quite indispensable to modern fisheries.

The principle of echo sounding is as follows: an oscillator installed in the bottom of the ship's hull sends out a narrow beam of sound waves which are reflected from the sea bottom as an echo which is then picked up by some form of receiver. Since the speed of sound in water is known (it is c. 1,500 m per second) one can calculate the water depth from the time taken by the sound waves (ship—sea bottom—ship). For instance, if the time taken is 1 second, then the depth of water is 1,500 divided by $2 = 750$ m. The depth is recorded on a broad strip of paper which

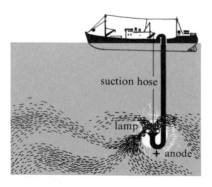

suction hose

lamp

+ anode

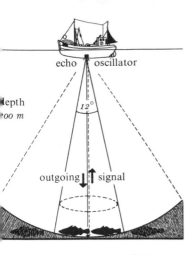

depth
·oo m

12°

echo   oscillator

outgoing ↕ signal

·h 1 m above   indistinct area
·ttom

passed slowly through an echo-sounding
·per-recorder. As soon as the pen or writer
·sses the zero line on the recording paper
·which denotes the sea surface) the signals
·e automatically sent out. The wave
·flected from the sea bottom is trans-
·rmed into alternative current and drawn
·y the recorder as an echo mark on the
·per; the distance of this mark from the
·ro line gives the relevant depth.

The oscillator sends out sound waves

with a high frequency (20–50 kilocycles)
(ultra sound waves). Evidently these sound
waves do not disturb the fish.

As the recording paper moves slowly
past the pen, the individual echo marks
together form a continuous depth curve,
which depicts in miniature the relief of the
sea bottom.

However, the echo trace not only gives a
measurement of the depth, for in fact the
sound waves more or less penetrate the
substrate, depending upon its reflecting
nature: a soft bottom reflects a soft echo.
One is therefore provided with an idea of
the nature of the bottom. Naturally, it is of
the greatest importance for the fisheries to
be able also to read off from the echo
trace the extent and depth of a fish swarm
(fish location).

Echo-sounders are adjustable to different depths ranges, e.g. 100–200 fathoms,
200–300 fathoms. In this way the whole
width of the paper can be made available
for the desired range.

Recent technical advances have resulted
in specially sensitive equipment capable of
locating aggregations of fish immediately
above the bottom. For, in addition to the
ordinary echo sounder trace, the fisherman
can also use a fish-finder, a cathode ray
tube which will show him an echo of the
fish shoal and of the bottom as horizontal
deflections from a vertical stripe of light.

echogram   fish-finder

·urface

·erring shoal

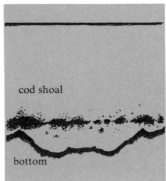

cod shoal

bottom

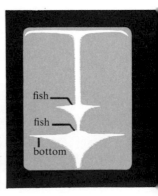

fish

fish

bottom

228

In recent years there has been increasing use of horizontal echo ranging. In this method an oscillator installed in the bottom of the ship sends out a narrow beam of sound pulses forwards and obliquely downwards (Sonar or Asdic, developed during the war for submarine detection).

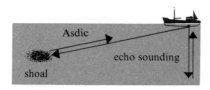

Horizontal echo ranging has been used, in particular, by the Norwegians for whale-catching and for the location of herring shoals. By using a movable Asdic oscillator a ship under way can sweep a fan-shaped area (up to 3 km).

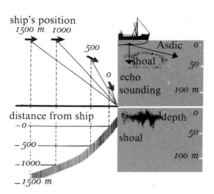

the distance of the shoal from the ship is plotted by the Asdic recorder

the shoal comes into the search area of the echo sounder

Horizontal ranging is particularly useful in mid-water trawling and purse seining. After further improvements have been made—and as soon as there is a drop in the cost of the equipment and its installation—this will also be a valuable aid to trawlers, for example in enabling them to detect and avoid obstacles on the sea floor

It is nowadays of great importance for the fisherman to be able to fix his position exactly, for only then can he find the good fishing areas, which are often very restricted. Considerable progress has been made in this field since the Second World War.

In western Europe 10 Decca chains have been set up, each consisting of a master station and three slave stations. The slaves arranged in the form of a triangle around the main station, are 200–300 km from it. The radio waves (differing from one another in wavelength, amplitude and phase) are sent out simultaneously by the main station and by the slaves. At certain points they are mutually reinforced or weakened by interference. If one plots these phase lines on a chart they will lie as firm position lines in hyperbolic curves around each Decca chain; they are numbered. Each Decca chain has a transmitting area of 250–500 sea miles; the areas of each transmitter overlap each other. The Decca navigator installed on the ship records on a decometer the position line on which the ship actually lies. The point where the position lines of two Decca chains cross will give the actual position of the ship with great accuracy.

Ship's radar is particularly important as an aid to navigation in the foggy northern fishing grounds where there is also the danger of icebergs. It can detect obstacles from a considerable distance away.

In addition, direction-finding equipment has been used on fishing vessels for many years. Here the ship takes bearings on the transmissions from two fixed radio stations.

THE FISHING INDUSTRY

It is only in coastal regions that fish can be landed in good condition or even alive. For longer fishing trips the catch has to be immediately killed, gutted, washed and stored between layers of crushed ice, salted or deep-frozen. The following section gives various examples of the different ways in which this raw material is handled and prepared.

Preservation by chilling

About 35–40 per cent of the world catch is marketed as fresh fish. The rest goes for salting, smoking, fillets, cans and fish meal. For transport from the landing places to the user the fresh fish is packed in wooden boxes holding 20–50 kg, with the addition of ice. Some species, such as plaice, trout and eel, can be transported alive in railway wagons or freight trucks equipped with tanks and artificial aeration.

Since the Second World War and as a result of the rapid development of refrigeration technique, there has been considerable progress in the maintenance and improvement of quality. Frozen fish products are now important to both the wholesale and the retail side of the industry.

During refrigeration at 0° to −5°C ice crystals form in the fish flesh. With slow freezing processes the crystals formed are fairly large and they change or destroy the muscle fibres and connective tissue. If, on the other hand, the temperature is reduced rapidly smaller crystals are formed and the flesh preserves its original characteristics. After freezing the whole fish is usually 'glazed', i.e. covered with a coating of ice by dipping it in water, and then kept in a refrigerator until dispatch. The final quality of the frozen product depends, among other things, on the freshness of the raw material which should, in fact, be frozen as soon as possible (within 2–3 days at the most). Modern fishing vessels are therefore equipped with deep-freezing plants for use at sea.

Stockfish

An old method of keeping fish for a long time is to remove the water by drying it in air, exposed to the sun and wind. Fishes of the cod group which contain little fat are particularly suitable for this purpose, but fatty fishes cannot be used as they easily liquefy.

In the Nordic countries cod and related fishes have long been made into stockfish. This is based on suitable climatic conditions and large cod stocks. In the preparation of stockfish, the fish are decapitated, gutted and hung on long wooden poles to dry in the air. By this means the water content of the flesh is reduced from 80% to 12–15%.

After drying, the fish are stacked one above the other, pressed into bales and kept in cool, dry, well ventilated stores until they are dispatched.

Before use, stockfish must be soaked for about 14 days in water containing soda and other chemicals. This causes the flesh to swell and increase to up to 700% of its dry weight.

Stockfish is an important product of the Nordic countries, and in particular of Norway (35,000–40,000 tons) and Iceland (6,000–9,000 tons) which satisfy much of the demand of countries in Europe and South America. Flatfishes, such as halibut and dab, are also dried and prepared as delicatessen products.

Preservation by salt

Salt also removes water from the flesh and thus acts as a preservative; at suitable concentrations it also inhibits the growth of putrefying organisms. By salting, fish can be not only preserved but at the same time transformed into a delicacy.

Salted herrings are an important product; after removal of the gills, gut, liver and heart the fish are packed in barrels between layers of salt. About one ton of salt is needed for 4 tons of herring. The salt removes water from the flesh so that mass of herring sinks and the barrels have to be re-packed and filled on land. The salted herrings are marketed under various names according to their size and quality; some are prepared in sauces with spices and other substances.

Cod, haddock, saithe and ling are usually cleaned on board the fishing vessel and salted as 'round fish' or split open (most of the backbone being removed). In this process they are prepared with 20–30% of salt.

Cod and ling may also be landed fresh and then salted. They are packed mechanically between layers of salt into the barrel. Within a short time they will be covered with the brine, owing to the removal of water from the tissues. They are then stored for 1–6 months in order to allow the product to ferment.

Klipfish

This is dried, split and salted fish. The highly salted fish are laid out to dry on timber or flat rocks.

When dried in the open the fish have to be brought in at night or during rainy weather to prevent them becoming damp. It is therefore quite usual to use drying sheds in which hot air is passed over the fish. With the combined action of the salt and the drying the fish lose a considerable amount of weight; 100 kg of fresh fish (decapitated and gutted) yields c. 40 kg of klipfisk.

The annual production of different countries is: Norway and Canada each c. 32,000 tons, Japan 11,000 tons, Faeroes 5,000–7,000 tons, Iceland 2,000–6,000 tons.

Smoking

The process of smoking not only acts as a preservative but also improves the taste of the fish. Certain components of the smoke kill the putrefying organisms chemically or at least inhibit their growth, while at the same time the tarry substances in the skin and flesh acquire an appetising golden-yellow colour and improve the scent and flavour. Sometimes the action of the natural smoke can be imitated by chemical means.

At one time the fish were suspended in a funnel-shaped chimney and exposed for 2–24 hours to the smoke from smouldering chips of wood from deciduous trees. Nowadays the fishing industry uses large modern smoking ovens, in which the temperature, smoke production and ventilation are automatically controlled, so that the product has a uniformly high quality.

There are two main methods of smoking fish: rapid hot smoking (at 80–100°C) and slow cold smoking (at c. 30°C). Salmon and salt herring are, for example, smoked cold, but mackerel and fresh or frozen herring undergo the hot smoking process. Almost every European country has its own specialities.

English and Scottish kippers are made by splitting the herring along the back, immersing it in brine for 15 minutes, drying and then smoking for 4–5 hours (or even longer). Red herring are complete salt herrings which are washed and then smoked for 4–6 weeks. The lengthy period of smoking gives a product that keeps very well.

'Kieler Sprotten' (Kiel sprats) are prepared from ungutted small herring and sprats. 'Schillerlocken' are the smoked, thin belly flaps of the spur-dog, while the dorsal side (smoked or fresh) is marketed as 'seeaal' (sea eel). Saithe are salted, smoked, slightly dyed and placed in oil for marketing as 'seelachs' (sea salmon) which is a popular substitute for smoked salmon. The Danish Bornholmers are hot smoked herring.

Eel, mackerel, salmon, haddock, halibut, flounder, dab and plaice are also smoked.

Apart from the actual fishes the fishing industry also smokes cod liver, oysters and mussels. Mildly salted and smoked roes of cod, herring and lumpsucker are also regarded as delicacies.

Fish meal and oil

As the fishing industry has developed it has become common practice to make use of the offal (head, fin, backbone and entrails) which was previously thrown away. 'Industrial fish' has come in as a new term since the Second World War.

This material would include anything landed by fishing vessels that was not suitable for human consumption, that is any fish surplus to market requirements or condemned on health grounds, as well as small crustaceans, starfishes etc.

Large processing plants can take such material, as well as the waste from smoking, filleting and canning factories, and use it for the preparation of fish meal and fish oil. In order to satisfy the growing demands of these fish meal factories there is now intensive trawling of shoal fishes just for this purpose (e.g. herring, capelin, sand-eels and Norway pout).

In the preparation of fish meal the raw material is first chopped up mechanically and then sterilised with steam. The water and oil are then pressed out, and the residue is more finely chopped and dried with hot air. Finally the resulting meal is ground, and strong magnets remove iron objects, such as fish hooks.

The finished product has a water content of 10–14%.

At one time fish meal was used primarily as fertiliser, but the high quality of the present-day product now makes it a valu-

industrial uses of fish

able, protein-rich fodder for agricultura and piscicultural use.

By using solvents (acetone, alcohol, etc it is possible to remove most of the fa from the raw fish or from fish meal.

In recent years investigations have als

een made on the possibility of using fish meal for human consumption. With support from the Food and Agricultural Organization of the United Nations, uccessful attempts have been made in hile and in several other countries.

Fish meal is tasteless and odourless after has been refined, but the raw material nd the intermediate products foul the air, nd so it is advisable to locate fish meal actories at some distance from human abitation.

The annual world production of fish meal has risen considerably in recent years, nd is now about 5 million tons, corresponding to 20 million tons of fresh fish, r about 33% of the total world catch. The rincipal producer is Peru with $c.$ 1 million ons. In Europe fish meal is mainly produced by Norway, Denmark, Britain and Germany.

Fish oil is extracted from fatty fishes, uch as herring, pilchard, menhaden, scad, nd to a lesser extent salmon and tunny. The raw material can either be first dried nd the oil extracted by solvents which re later removed by distillation or it can e cooked and pressed, and the oil then emoved from the resulting liquid. The esidual material is dried and ground into sh meal.

Fish oil is used in large quantities by the margarine industry, but it also has several other uses, such as for shoe polish, oil aints, candles and linoleum. The annual vorld production is $c.$ 1,000,000 tons, most f which comes from Peru and the U.S.A., nd in Europe from Norway, Iceland, Denmark and Germany.

Another important product of the fishing ndustry is liver oil. This is produced mainly from the livers of cod, haddock, aithe, tunny, halibut, rays and sharks, n which the liver accounts for 5–10%

of the total body weight (in the basking shark up to 30%).

The livers are removed from the fish on board ship and either taken back under refrigeration or, in the case of long voyages, they are processed in a special plant on the ship. The livers are treated with superheated steam so that the cells release their content of oil; a centrifuge is then used to separate the oil from the liver residue. Other methods are based on the use of acids or low temperatures.

Liver oil was formerly used mainly for various technical purposes, but nowadays it is employed in the pharmaceutical industry in the production of vitamin preparations. Thus, for example, 1 gram of halibut liver oil contains $c.$ 50,000 international units (I.U.) of vitamin A, and $c.$ 1,500 I.U. of vitamin D, while 1 gram of cod liver oil has 1,000 I.U. vitamin A and 100 I.U. vitamin D.

The annual world production of liver oil has risen to at least 60,000—70,000 tons, Britain and Norway being the main producers in Europe.

Canned products

Approximately 10% of the world catch of fish is canned. The principal species used are herring, mackerel and salmon. Marinades containing salt and vinegar are used for various preparations, but these can only be kept for a limited period and are intended for quick consumption. Cold marinades, as used for Bismarck herring, rollmops etc, are usually avoided, whereas heated marinades give a product with better keeping qualities.

Only sterilised cans will keep more or less indefinitely.

FISHERY BIOLOGY

Vignette from Volume 1 of
the Report of the Challenger
Expedition, 1873–1876

Even in ancient times there were certain people who took an interest in marine life and the natural history of edible fishes. However, it was only in the last century, after detailed investigations had been started in certain countries, that marine biology developed into an independent science with many diverse interests. Between 1800 and 1900 there were over 70 scientific expeditions which had the task of collecting basic knowledge on life in the sea. Using scientific equipment and methods these investigations were the necessary forerunner for all the later, more applied research. The aim of fisheries research is to find the most rational methods of bringing ashore the 'harvest of the sea' in usable condition and in the greatest possible amounts.

To achieve this it is, of course, necessary to carry out detailed investigations on the natural history of the edible or economically valuable fishes. Fisheries biology therefore works primarily on problems of nutrition, growth and reproduction of economic fishes, and on their environmental conditions, in order to provide new knowledge that will help the advance of practical fisheries. Only in this way can an answer be found to the many biological and economic problems that crop up, and a basis established for the development of new fishing methods and the formulation of appropriate national and international fisheries regulations.

The International Council for the Exploration of the Sea was established in 1902, and it has its headquarters in Copenhagen. It consists of representatives of European countries engaged in fishing and holds a meeting each year at which new investigations are planned. These are then carried out by the research vessels and in the marine laboratories of the member nations.

The following section contains a brief account of the principal methods employed in fisheries biology.

Age determination

For this purpose the fisheries biologist can use the scales, the bones and the otoliths.

The scales grow in proportion to the growth of the body. Even with the relatively low magnification provided by an ordinary lens one can see (particularly in transmitted light) the narrow and wider growth rings. During winter a fish usually grows very slowly, and so at this period of poor food supply the rings lie close to one another. In summer, on the other hand, broader circular bands are formed. A single annual ring is made up of a summer and a winter growth zone.

In many cases it is still not entirely clear how these rings are formed. The rhythm of ring deposition appears to be dependent both upon internal (nutrition, maturity, etc) and external factors (e.g. climatic).

The otoliths are calcareous deposits in

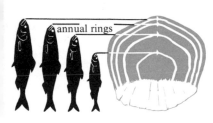

annual rings

the labyrinth of the auditory organ of fishes (see p. 61) from which the age can be read. They often show a very distinct alternation of dark and pale zones. The winter zones stand out particularly clearly after the thickness of the otoliths has been reduced by grinding.

transverse section of cod otolith annual rings

The bones also undergo periodic growth, so they too can be used in age determination. The most suitable for this purpose are the vertebrae and the bones of the gill covers.

Age determination enables the fishery biologist to determine the growth rates of a given species. The fishes caught are first sorted into age groups (O, I, II, III, etc) and then measured. It is then possible to calculate the average length of the individual groups. Lengths can then be plotted on a graph against time (age). From such a curve it is possible to read off the growth rates of the fishes and the productivity of a water mass. A large amount of material is used in order to reduce sources of error.

Feeding investigations

Direct observations and examination of the gut contents will provide accurate information on the variety and amount of food eaten by a fish. The distribution and biology of the food animals (or food plants) are also of interest. The bottom grab is an important piece of equipment used in the biological investigations of a fishing area. This is a relatively small piece of apparatus which is lowered to the bottom where it grabs a fixed area of the sea floor which can then be taken ashore. From such samples it is possible to determine the distribution of the bottom fauna and flora, with their many different species.

After it had been established that plant and animal plankton provide the basic food supply for all life in the open sea, the investigation of plankton developed into an extensive independent discipline.

This is a field in which there must be close co-operation between zoologists, botanists, physiologists, etc, if the complicated interrelationships are to be clarified. The botanists, for example, work primarily on problems of phytoplankton production in different parts of the sea and study the physical and chemical factors which in-

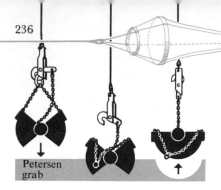

plankton net

Petersen grab

fluence the scale of production: sunshine, currents, cycle of nutrient salts, etc. The build-up of organic substances by the phytoplankton can be followed by using glass flasks in which the nutrient salts contain radioactive carbon.

Feeding investigations have shown that many fish populations show signs of undernutrition. The denser the population, the greater is the competition for food. The growth rate of fishes is, however, dependent upon the amount of available food and is therefore relatively low in overpopulated areas. This is one of the reasons why the growth of a species may vary considerably in different parts of its range. When a population is reduced by fishing, the remaining fish in many cases grow much faster and the fisheries yield increases; around 1920 the flounder population in the southern North Sea was very dense, and at that time a five year-old flounder had a maximum length of 20 cm. Nowadays, under the influence of intensive fishing, a specimen of the same age will be over 30 cm long.

Fish tagging

In order to find out about the migrations of a given species, captured individuals are marked or tagged and then released. Reports of recaptured specimens will then provide data on which the direction and speed of migration can be calculated. In such marking experiments different kinds of tags are used, according to the anatomy and habits of the species involved.

Thus, flatfishes are usually marked with two circular tags of ebonite or plastic which are attached by a silver wire running through the dorsal musculature. Roundbodied fishes are sometimes marked with similar tags, attached to the gill cover or behind the dorsal fin.

Another method uses small plastic tubes containing paper slips on which the necessary information for the finder is printed. These are also attached by a thin silver wire running through the musculature at the front or hind end of the dorsal fin.

Shoaling fishes that are mainly caught for processing into fish meal are marked with small metal plates that are introduced into the body cavity of the fish or inserted beneath its skin. These tags are later collected from the fish meal by strong electro-magnets installed in the fish-processing factory.

This method was developed as a means of estimating the strength of population and its 'mortality due to fishing'. Its use is based on a knowledge of the intensity of fishing (fishing time in hours per unit area). For this method it is essential to know the exact place and time of the catch.

Fish tags are marked with letters and figures, and often also with the address of a research station. When returning the tags or the marked fishes the time and place of capture must be given. The return of tags is usually acknowledged by a monetary reward.

A fish tag is only usable if it fulfils the following conditions: it must not (or only slightly) irritate the fish or in any way restrict its freedom of movement, and it

Marked Tunny hook. When pulled in the cast is torn off.

must at the same time be durable. The success of these investigations depends primarily on the tagged fish behaving completely normally, so that it is not at a disadvantage in relation to other members of the species in the struggle for existence and therefore takes part just as actively in the feeding and spawning migrations. Only under these conditions will the recaptures yield valid conclusions on the state of a given population.

The tag must also be very conspicuous so that it is not overlooked by the fishermen.

For these marking experiments, only completely healthy fish should be used, immediately after capture. Fishes which die quickly in the air (herring, mackerel) present special difficulties for marking. Fishes that live at great depths are very difficult and time-consuming; they have to be brought to the surface very slowly so that they can become adapted to the changes in water pressure. This is one of the main reasons, for example, why the migrations of the redfish have been so little investigated.

The ratio of re-captures is often surprisingly high, particularly when one thinks that in spite of every precaution a

certain number die, the tags are lost or not reported. Thus, over 40% of the plaice tagged in the North Sea are re-captured.

In addition to information on the movements of the fish, the re-capture ratio also gives an idea of the percentage of mortality due to fishing, which is dependent upon the intensity of fishing.

Investigation of races

Within their range of distribution many fish species form a number of geographical races, which may in turn be split up into numerous local forms. The different races of herring provide one of the best known examples; these can be distinguished by their different areas and periods of spawning (see herring, p. 64). In many fjords there are small local populations of herring, which are stationary, whereas the oceanic forms undertake very extensive spawning and feeding migrations.

The identification of the different races is often very difficult. Many of the characters can only be recognised statistically and so large numbers must be examined and measured. The number of vertebrae and of dorsal and anal fin rays are typical identification characters.

It often happens, however, that the numerical ranges overlap: thus, Race A may have 78–81 vertebrae, Race B 80–83, and so on.

In certain species the form of the growth rings on the scales or otoliths can also be used as identification characters. In recent years a start has been made in examining the blood groups of the different popula-

cod tagged in their spawning grounds

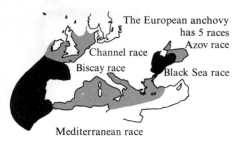

The European anchovy has 5 races

Channel race
Biscay race
Azov race
Black Sea race
Mediterranean race

tions. The blood sample can be taken directly from the heart of the living fish, which can then be marked and released.

Research on reproduction

Problems involving the recruitment of fish populations are of considerable interest, especially from the practical fisheries viewpoint. These include spawning migrations, reproduction and larval development.

In order to ensure that populations are maintained it is in many cases necessary to protect the spawning grounds and to restrict the capture of spawning fish. In the very prolific pelagic fishes, however, the number of eggs laid is less important for the future density of the population; here it is the environmental conditions (climatic, hydrographic, predators of eggs and larvae) that are more important in the early stages of development.

Fish populations and fishery yields

The wealth of the seas is not inexhaustible. It has been shown that fishing that is too intensive may result in 'overfishing'. In some areas the yield has decreased and fewer large fish are caught than in former times. In order to stop the impoverishment of a population it may be necessary to introduce protective regulations (a minimum size, closed seasons, closed areas, etc.). It is one of the most important tasks

of fisheries research to find out and recommend the measures which are most likely to prove successful.

In order to demonstrate clearly the type of problems involved, let us examine in more detail a couple of sample fish populations. In the first example we will assume that we have a population with an annual accretion of 1,000 individuals which have survived the larval period and have reached an age of one year. As a result of the attacks of predators and through disease (natural mortality) their numbers become reduced in the succeeding years by a certain percentage (in our example by 40%) while at the same time the survivors increase in weight. Our example may then be summarised as in the following table:

Table 1

Age group	Number	Individual weight	Total weight per age group
1	1000	0·030 kg	30 kg
2	600	0·200 kg	120 kg
3	360	0·400 kg	144 kg
4	216	0·800 kg	173 kg
5	130	1·400 kg	**182 kg**
6	78	2·000 kg	156 kg
7	47	3·000 kg	141 kg
8	28	4·400 kg	123 kg
9	17	5·400 kg	92 kg
10	10	6·100 kg	61 kg
11	6	6·600 kg	40 kg
12	4	7·000 kg	28 kg
13	2	7·200 kg	14 kg
14	1	7·300 kg	7 kg

Population: **2499** fishes; Weight: **1311** kg.

This table gives the following results: on the assumption that 1,000 young fish arrive each year and that there is a natural mortality of 40%, the population will always have about 2,500 individuals, distributed in 14 age groups.

From the fisheries viewpoint, however, interest is not so much in the number of individuals as in the total weight of an age group. As will be seen from the weights column, the highest total weight is reached by age group 5. In the subsequent groups, growth can no longer keep pace with the mortality; although the weight of the individual fishes increases rapidly, the total weight of each age group decreases. If it were possible in practice one should therefore catch from this population all the 5 year old fishes and none of the others.

In this example we have, however, assumed a natural mortality of 40%, so that the table did not become too long. If the mortality rate had been lower the optimal total weight would only have been reached at a higher age group. Appropriate investigations have shown that in nature the natural mortality is considerably lower. On the other hand, many fish species are subject to fishing. The total mortality of an economically important fish species is therefore the sum of the natural mortality and the losses due to fishing.

In the next example we have assumed a natural mortality of 20% and a 'fisheries mortality' of 40%. We will now try to find out which method of fishing would be most

suitable for this particular population. For instance, using a fine-mesh net we could catch all the fish from age group 2 upwards. But would this be expedient?

The following table gives the fishing yield with nets of two different meshes; with a mesh of 80 mm all the fish of age group 2 and upwards could be caught, with a mesh of 140 mm, all the fish of age group 4 upwards. The intensity of fishing must be kept at the same level throughout the year.

This table shows that with wide mesh nets the fishery yield would be about 58.6% higher. In addition, it shows that this intensively fished population has shrunk to 11 or 12 year classes whereas the unfished population of Table I contained 14 age groups. In other words the old, large individuals have become scarcer.

These examples only provide a very simplified scheme of what happens in practice. Thus, the percentage mortality is highest among young fish and it may fluctuate considerably from year to year. In addition, these examples do not take account of the fact that in each year the number of developing fry is very variable and so the increment of young fish is not

Table 11

	Mesh size 80 mm				Mesh size 140 mm			
Age group	Population reduction	Natural mortality	Number caught	Weight of catch	Population reduction	Natural mortality	Number caught	Weight of catch
1	1000–800	200	0	**0·0**	1000–800	200	0	**0·0**
2	800–384	126	290	**87·0**	800–640	160	0	**0·0**
3	384–184	61	139	**83·4**	640–512	128	0	**0·0**
4	184–88	29	67	**73·7**	512–246	81	185	**203·5**
5	88–42	14	32	**54·4**	246–118	39	89	**151·3**
6	42–20	7	15	**37·5**	118–57	19	42	**105·0**
7	20–10	3	7	**25·9**	57–27	9	21	**77·7**
8	10–5	2	3	**14·7**	27–13	4	10	**49·0**
9	5–2	1	2	**15·0**	13–6	2	5	**28·8**
10	2–1	0	1	**6·4**	6–3	1	2	**12·7**
11	1–0	0	1	**6·8**	3–1	1	1	**6·8**
12					1–0	0	1	**7·1**
			yield in kg: **404·8**				yield in kg: **641·9**	

constant, hence the size of the different year groups is not always the same. This applies particularly to herring, and also to flatfishes, in which good years alternate with poor years. The survival of the newly hatched larvae depends very largely on environmental conditions. In one year the conditions in the North Sea may be suitable for the brood, in another year in the Barents Sea.

In order to produce an analysis of practical value of a fish population in a given fishing area, the biologist must investigate the following points: the rate of growth of the species concerned, the frequency of the individual age groups (or the age composition of the population), the percentage mortality due to natural causes and to fishing, and the intensity of fishing.

There are often great practical difficulties in collecting these basic data. The populations are often fished by several nations and so international cooperation between scientists is quite essential. In addition, the different countries must not only produce detailed fishery statistics but also data on other points, such as the number of fishing vessels, the fishing gear and so on.

The individual fish populations should be used according to a uniform and optimal system. Unfortunately this is often prevented by social, economic and political differences between the countries involved.

In the North Sea, for example, the populations of cod, haddock, whiting and plaice are intensively fished. By using nets with a large mesh and forbidding the landing of small fish, a considerable increase in the fishery yield could be obtained in the course of a few years, if only the different countries concerned would come to an agreement.

In certain cases a reduction in the intensity of fishing could also result in an increase in yield. The present high percentage of mortality due to fishing could decrease and hence the numbers of the higher, more valuable age groups would increase.

These few examples should help to show the economic importance of modern research on population dynamics.

Subsidiary Identification Keys

Herring-like Fishes 64
Pipefishes 92
Fishes of the cod group with 3 dorsal fins 97
Wrasse 128

Mackerel family 139
Cottids 164
Flatfishes 172

Index of English names

Albacore, False 144
Anchovy 70
Angler 194
Argentine, Larger 80
   Lesser 80
   Sheppy 72

Bass 123
Beryx 120
Bib 104
Blackfish 28
Blenny, Butterfly 150
   Montagu's 150
   Snake 150
   Tompot 150
   Yarrell's 150
Bluemouth 160
Bonito, Oceanic 146
   Plain 147
Bream, Black Sea 127
   Ray's 124
   Red Sea 126
Brill 174
Bullhead, Norway 165
Butterfish 150

Capelin 80
Catfish, Spotted 152
Clingfish, Two-spotted 26
Cod 98
   Greenland 102
   Polar 102
   Poor- 106
Corkwing 130
Cottus, Four-horned 166
Crab, Edible 202
Crawfish 201

Dab 182
   Long rough 180

Dealfish 120
Dogfish, Black-mouthed 47
   Larger spotted 46
   Lesser spotted 46
Dragonet 136
   Spotted 136

Eel, Common 82
   Conger 86
   Silver 82
   Yellow 82
Eelpout 154
   Vahl's 154

Father lasher 164
Flounder 188
Flying fish 91
Forkbeard, Greater 112

Garfish 88
Goby, Black 156
   Common 158
   Crystal 158
   Fries's 156
   Jeffreys's 26
   Painted 158
   Rock 156
   Sand 158
   Transparent 158
   Two-spot 157
Goldsinny 130
Grenadier 95
Gunnel 150
Gurnard, Grey 162
   Red 162
   Streaked 162
   Tub 162

Haddock 104
   Norway 160

Hagfish 32
Hake 116
Halibut 178
   Greenland 180
Hatchetfish 72
Herring 64

Jelly cat 152
John Dory 122

Lamprey, River 32
   Sea 32
Ling 114
   Blue 114
   Spanish 114
Lobster 199
   Norway 200
Lumpsucker 168

Mackerel 140
   Frigate 148
   Spanish 142
Mako 22
Meagre 124
Megrim 176
Monkfish 50
Mullet, Golden 138
   Grey 138
   Red 124
   Thick-lipped 138
   Thin-lipped 138
Mussel 206

Octopus, Common 204
   Lesser 204
Ogac 102
Opah 120
Oyster 206
   Portuguese 206

Pandora 126
Pelamid 146
Pilchard 70
Pipefish, Broad-nosed 92
    Great 93
    Nilsson's 92
    Snake 94
    Straight-nosed 94
    Worm 94
Piper 162
Plaice 184
Pogge 166
Pollack 110
Porbeagle 36
Pout, Norway 108
    Silvery 112
Prawn, Baltic 196
    Deep-sea 196
    Dublin Bay 200

Rabbitfish 58
Ray, Blonde 21
    Cuckoo 21
    Eagle 58
    Fylla's 52
    Marbled Electric 50
    Painted 21
    Pale 56
    Sandy 21
    Shagreen 56
    Spotted 21
    Starry 52
    Sting 58
    Thornback 52
    Undulate 21
Redfish 160
Rock cook 130

Rockling, Five-bearded 118
    Four-bearded 118
    Three-bearded 118
Saithe 110
Salmon 74
Sand-eel 132
    Greater 132
    Smooth 132
Sand-smelt 136
Sardine 70
Saury 90
Scad 123
Scaldfish 174
Sea-horses 94
Sea Scorpion 166
Sea Snail 169
    Montagu's 169
Shad, Allis 72
    Twaite 72
Shanny 150
Shark, Basking 38
    Blue 42
    Frilled 21
    Greenland 48
    Six-gilled 21
Shrimp 196
Skate 54
    Long-nosed 56
Skipper 90
Smelt 80
Smooth hound 40
Snipefish 23
Sole 192
    Lemon 190
    Sand 192
Solenette 192
Spider-crab 202

Sprat 68
Spur-dog 44
Squid, Northern 204
Stickleback, Sea 170
    Ten-spined 170
    Three-spined 170
Sturgeon 62
Sunfish 194
Swordfish 148

Tadpole-fish 112
Thresher 40
Tope 40
Topknot 176
    Norwegian 176
Torsk 116
Trout 78
    Rainbow 78
Tunny 142
    Long-fin 144
Turbot 172

Velvet Belly 46

Weever, Greater 134
    Lesser 134
Whiting 106
    Blue 108
Witch 190
Wolf-fish 152
Wrasse, Ballan 128
    Cuckoo 128
    Rainbow 132
    Scale-rayed 130
Wreckfish 28

Index of Scientific names

Acantholabrus palloni
    130
Acipenser sturio 62
Agonus cataphractus 166
Alopias vulpinus 40
Alosa alosa 72
    fallax 72
Ammodytes marinus 132
    tobianus 132
Anarhichas lupus 152
    minor 152

Anguilla anguilla 82
Aphia minuta 158
Argentina silus 80
    sphyraena 80
Argyropelecus olfersi 72
Argyrosomus regium 124
Arnoglossus laterna 174
Artediellus uncinatus 164
Aspitrigla cuculus 162
Atherina presbyter 136
Auxis thazard 148

Belone belone 88
Beryx decadactylus 120
Blennius gattorugine 150
    ocellaris 150
    pholis 150
Boreogadus saida 102
Brama brama 124
Brosme brosme 116
Buenia jeffreysi 26
Buglossidium luteum
    192

Callionymus lyra 136
    maculatus 136
Cancer pagurus 202
Centrolabrus exoletus 130
Centrolophus niger 28
Centrophorus squamosus 22
Cetorhinus maximus 38
Chaparrudo flavescens 157
Chimaera monstrosa 58
Chirolophis ascanii 150
Chlamydoselachus anguineus 21
Ciliata mustela 118
Clupea harengus 64
Conger conger 86
Coris julis 132
Coryphaenoides rupestris 95
Coryphoblennius galerita 150
Crangon vulgaris 196
Crassostrea angulata 206
Crenilabrus melops 130
Crenimugil labrosus 138
Crystallogobius linearis 158
Ctenolabrus rupestris 130
Cyclopterus lumpus 168
Cypsilurus heterurus 91

Dasyatis pastinaca 58
Dicentrarchus labrax 123
Diplecogaster bimaculata 26

Eledone cirrhosa 204
Engraulis encrasicolus 70
Entelurus aequoreus 94
Etmopterus spinax 46
Euthynnus alletteratus 144
Eutrigla gurnardus 162

Gadiculus argenteus 112
Gadus morrhua 98
    ogac 102
Gaidropsarus vulgaris 118
Galeorhinus galeus 40
Galeus melastomus 47
Gasterosteus aculeatus 170
Glyptocephalus cynoglossus 190
Gobius friesi 156
    minutus 158
    niger 156
    paganellus 156
Gymnammodytes cicerellus 133
    semisquamatus 132
Gymnocanthus triscuspis 164

Helicolenus dactylopterus 160
Hexanchus griseus 21
Hippoglossoides platessoides 180
Hippoglossus hippoglossus 178
Homarus vulgaris 199
Hyperoplus lanceolatus 132

Icelus bicornis 164
Isurus oxyrinchus 22

Katsuwonus pelamis 146

Labrus berggylta 128
    mixtus 128
Lamna nasus 36
Lampetra fluviatilis 32
Lampris guttatus 120
Leander adspersus 196
Lepidorhombus whiffiagonis 176
Leptoclinus maculatus 150
Leptogonus decagonus 166
Limanda limanda 182
Liparis liparis 169
    montagui 169
Liza auratus 138
    ramàda 138
Loligo forbesi 204
Lophius piscatorius 194
Lumpenus lampretaeformis 150
Lycenchelys sarsii 154
Lycichthys denticulatus 152
Lycodes vahli 154

Macrorhamphosus scolopax 23
Maia squinado 202
Mallotus villosus 80
Maurolicus muelleri 72
Melanogrammus aeglefinus 104
Merlangius merlangus 106
Merluccius merluccius 116
Micromesistius poutassou 108
Microstomus kitt 190
Mola mola 194
Molva dypterygia 114
    macrophthalma 114
    molva 114
Mullus surmuletus 124
Mustelus mustelus 40
Myliobatis aquila 58
Myoxocephalus scorpius 164
Mytilus edulis 206
Myxine glutinosa 32

Nephrops norvegicus 200
Nerophis lumbriciformis 94
    ophidion 94

Octopus vulgaris 204
Oncocottus quadricornis 166
Orcynopsis unicolor 147
Osmerus eperlanus 80
Ostrea edulis 206

Pagellus bogaraveo 126
    erythrinus 126
Palinurus vulgaris 201
Pandalus borealis 196
Pegusa lascaris 192
Petromyzon marinus 32
Pholis gunnellus 150
Phrynorhombus norvegicus 176
Phycis blennioides 112
Platichthys flesus 188
Pleuronectes platessa 184
Pollachius pollachius 110
    virens 110
Polyprion americanus 28
Pomatoschistus microps 158
    pictus 158
Prionace glauca 42
Pterycombus brama 124
Pungitius pungitius 170

Raja batis 54
    brachyura 21
    circularis 21
    clavata 52
    fullonica 56
    fyllae 52
    lintea 56
    microocellata 21
    montagui 21
    naevus 21
    oxyrinchus 56
    radiata 52
    undulata 21
Raniceps raninus 112
Reinhardtius hippoglossoides 180
Rhinonemus cimbrius 118

Salmo gairdneri 78
    salar 74
    trutta 78
Saıda sarda 146
Sardina pilchardus 70
Scomber colias 142
    scombrus 140
Scomberesox saurus 90
Scophthalmus maximus 172
    rhombus 174
Scyliorhinus caniculus 46
    stellaris 46
Sebastes marinus 160
    viviparus 160
Solea solea 192
Somniosus microcephalus 48
Spinachia spinachia 170
Spondyliosoma cantharus 127
Sprattus sprattus 68
Squalus acanthias 44
Squatina squatina 50
Syngnathus acus 92
    rostellatus 92
    typhle 92

Taurulus bubalis 166
    lilljeborgi 165
Thunnus alalunga 144
    thynnus 142
Torpedo marmorata 50
Trachinus draco 134
    vipera 134
Trachypterus arcticus 120
Trachurus trachurus 123
Trigla lucerna 162
    lyra 162
Trigloporus lastoviza 162
Triglops pingeli 164
Trisopterus esmarkii 108
    luscus 104
    minutus 106

Xiphias gladius 148

Zeugopterus punctatus 176
Zeus faber 122
Zoarces viviparus 154